healthy eating

healthy eating

Using the glycemic index for optimal health

Introductory text by
Dr Susanna Holt

BARNES & NOBLE

NEW YORK

contents

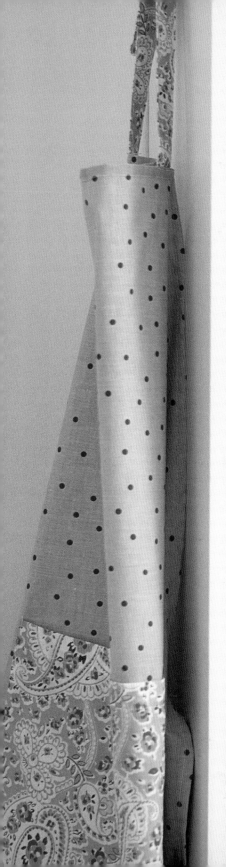

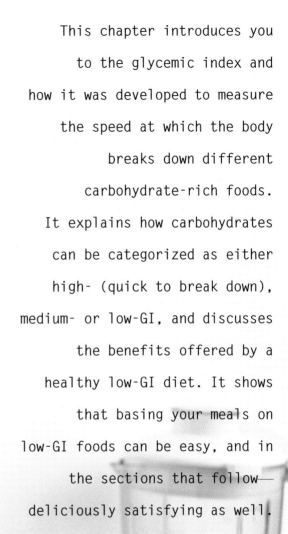

This chapter introduces you to the glycemic index and how it was developed to measure the speed at which the body breaks down different carbohydrate-rich foods. It explains how carbohydrates can be categorized as either high- (quick to break down), medium- or low-GI, and discusses the benefits offered by a healthy low-GI diet. It shows that basing your meals on low-GI foods can be easy, and in the sections that follow— deliciously satisfying as well.

healthy eating
the low GI way

healthy eating
the low GI way

Over the last century, lifestyle and dietary patterns in industrialized societies have made it increasingly easy for people to become overweight and develop serious health problems. In general, people have become less active and now eat more highly processed food than they did in the past. Scientific studies have revealed that this combination is unhealthy. To combat these negative effects health authorities recommend that people reduce the amount of saturated fat they eat and mostly choose carbohydrate-rich foods that have a low glycemic index (GI).

The glycemic index was developed 20 years ago in order to measure the effects that different carbohydrate-rich foods had on people's blood sugar levels. This research revealed that less refined carbohydrate-rich foods (low GI) are digested more slowly than highly processed ones (high GI). A low-GI diet with a low saturated-fat content has many advantages: it helps control blood sugar, cholesterol and triglyceride levels; it is more filling and can help make weight control easier; and can offer long-term health benefits such as a reduced risk of developing cardiovascular disease, type 2 diabetes and certain types of cancers.

carbohydrate: friend or foe?

If you're confused about the place of carbohydrate in a healthy diet, then you're not alone. Misinformation about the health effects of carbohydrates is widespread. Certain publications have claimed that carbohydrates are responsible for many of the serious health problems that plague modern societies. However, not all carbohydrate-rich foods are the same. Some are more healthy than others, including many low-GI foods. The recent carbohydrate backlash, particularly popular in the US, is due to the perception that high-carbohydrate, low-fat diets have not helped people lose weight or stopped them from gaining weight over the long term. However, the continuing rise in obesity in industrialized societies is not caused by carbohydrate-rich foods alone—it is due to the combination of certain types of foods and modern work and lifestyle habits that make it much easier for us to gain weight than lose it.

During the 1980s and 1990s, health authorities recommended that people adopt low-fat diets based on fruit, vegetables and grain-based foods. During this time, many people misinterpreted these recommendations as meaning that all types of fatty foods were undesirable and that any type of low-fat cabohydrate-rich food was desirable. The food industry also responded by developing low-fat varieties of many processed foods; including cookies, sweets and other snack foods.

At the same time, some people mistakenly believed that they could eat as much pasta, rice, bread and potatoes as they wanted without gaining weight. While it is true that the human body is a remarkably sophisticated piece of machinery, it still has to obey the normal laws of chemistry. We can't escape the basic fact that if we eat more calories than we need—from any type of food—we will store extra body fat and gain weight.

It is true that some types of carbohydrate-rich foods are easier to over-eat and promote body fat storage to a greater degree than others. So, concern about some types of carbohydrate-rich foods is warranted, but restricting your intake of all carbohydrate-rich foods is not necessary. You just need to focus on eating nutritious low-GI foods most of the time.

what is carbohydrate?

Carbohydrate, like fat and protein, is a vital nutrient found in foods and drinks. After we consume carbohydrate, it is digested and glucose sugar is released into our bloodstream, providing our brain, organs and muscles with energy. In fact, the human body's main source of energy is this glucose sugar.

There are three main types of carbohydrates in foods: sugars, starches and fiber. Sugars and starches provide us with most of our energy, and fiber can influence how quickly sugar and starch are digested. Sugars are the smallest form of carbohydrate, while starches and fibers are larger molecules made up of many individual sugar units linked together in chains. Whenever we eat sugar or starch, our digestive processes work to break these molecules (or compounds) down into their individual sugar units (glucose, galactose, fructose), which are small enough to be absorbed into the bloodstream. Although fiber is also made up of chains of sugars, the types of bonds that link its sugars together are not broken down by human digestive systems, so the sugars in fiber are not an important source of energy. Different types of sugars, starches and fibers occur naturally in foods, and they differ in the type and number of sugar units they contain.

In the past, starches were called complex carbohydrates and sugars were called simple carbohydrates due to the differences in their size and structure.

It was assumed that larger starches would require a longer time to be digested and cause a slower rise in blood glucose than smaller (simple) sugars. However, when scientists measured the blood glucose (glycemic) responses produced by different foods they found that this assumption wasn't always true. Some starchy foods, such as white bread and potatoes, cause a much bigger rise in your blood sugar level than some sugar-rich foods, such as milk, yogurt and certain types of fruit. This surprising discovery led to the invention of the glycemic index—a way of separating carbohydrate-rich foods into low, medium and high categories according to their blood sugar responses. Diets based on low-GI foods which produce lower, sustained blood glucose responses are particularly beneficial for people with diabetes, but can also offer health benefits for most people.

how does carbohydrate affect insulin?

In healthy people, a meal that contains enough carbohydrate to cause the blood's glucose level to rise stimulates the release of insulin into the bloodstream. Insulin is a hormone made in the pancreas that causes the body to take up (or absorb) the nutrients being released into the bloodstream from the digested food. Typically within the first 2–3 hours following a meal, insulin enables the body to soak up the nutrients circulating in the bloodstream, and promotes fat storage and the use of glucose sugar for fuel. Any extra glucose sugar that is not needed for immediate energy needs is stored as glycogen in the liver and muscles, and can be broken down by the body at a later time to top up its energy levels.

Blood glucose response curves for equal-carbohydrate portions of three different foods

This graph illustrates the typical differences seen in the blood glucose responses produced by high- and low-GI foods. High-GI foods, such as glucose sugar and white bread, are quickly digested and produce a fast rush of glucose into the bloodstream. Subsequently, there is a large fall in blood glucose, due to the effects of insulin. In contrast, low-GI starchy foods, such as barley and grainy breads, produce a smaller and more gradual rise and fall in the blood's glucose level.

The amount of insulin released after a meal is usually proportional to the meal's blood glucose response. High-GI foods produce a larger rise in blood glucose and insulin levels than low- and medium-GI foods. In healthy people, a relatively high level of glucose and insulin in the blood reduces the amount of fat the body can use as fuel. Consequently, diets based on low-GI carbohydrate-rich foods have been shown to promote greater weight (body fat) loss than high-GI diets with a similar calorie content.

what is the glycemic index?

In the early 1980s, two Canadian scientists published the first glycemic index (GI)—a table that ranked carbohydrate-containing foods according to the blood sugar responses they produced in healthy people. The aim of developing this index was to help make it easier for people with diabetes to find foods that produce lower blood-glucose responses (i.e. low-GI foods) to control their blood sugar level better.

Since the first glycemic index was published, scientists have measured the GI values of hundreds of foods. The GI shows, for example, that highly processed foods, such as white bread, puffed grains or white rice produce much higher blood glucose responses than equal-carbohydrate portions of pasta or apples. High-GI foods contain rapidly digested carbohydrate that produces a spike—a fast and large rise in blood sugar—followed by a quick crash. In contrast, low-GI foods contain carbohydrate that is digested at a slower, steadier rate and produces a lower rise and fall in blood glucose. The GI is now the largest index available of any metabolic response produced by foods and is very useful for helping people lower the overall GI of their diet to help improve their health.

how are GI values measured?

To measure a food's GI value, a fixed portion of this test food is fed to a group of at least eight healthy people after they have fasted overnight. A small blood sample is collected from each person before they start eating the food, then additional blood samples are collected at regular time points over the next 2 hours. The total rise in blood glucose produced by that food over the 2-hour period is then measured in each person. This procedure is repeated on another day after the same people are fed a portion of pure glucose sugar dissolved in water (the reference food) that contains the same amount of digestible carbohydrate as the test food. A GI value is calculated for each person by expressing the total blood sugar response produced by the test food as a percentage of the blood sugar response produced by the

THE LOW-GI ADVANTAGE IN ACTION

Imagine you ate a ham and salad sandwich for lunch that was made from white bread, then you ate a processed fruit bar and drank a bottle of sports drink (all high-GI foods). Although you'd initially feel satisfied, you'd probably feel hungry again within the next 2 hours.

However, if you had eaten a sandwich made from dense wholegrain bread, a whole apple and a small tub of yogurt (all low-GI foods), you would probably not feel hungry again for 3–4 hours.

Although the two different lunches contain similar amounts of energy, the types of carbohydrate they contain produce very different blood sugar responses, which partly explains why one is more sustaining than the other.

GI CATEGORIES

- *Low GI foods: ≤ 55*
- *Medium GI foods: 56–69*
- *High GI foods: ≥ 70*

COMPARISON OF COMMON FOODS

HIGHER GI	GI value	LOWER GI	GI value
Bran flakes breakfast cereal	74	Bran cereal pellets	30
Whole wheat breakfast cereal cookies	69	Whole wheat and bran breakfast cereal cookies	57
Instant oatmeal from quick-cooking oats	82	Traditional oatmeal from whole oats	52*
White or whole wheat sandwich bread	75	Wholegrain soy and flaxseed breads (with visible grains)	44*
Watermelon	76	Apple	38*
Raisins	64	Prunes, dried apple or dried apricots	30*
Rice milk	92	Cows' milk, plain, average of all types	29
Gluten-free corn pasta, boiled	78	Regular durum wheat pasta, boiled	44*
Rice noodle, dried, boiled	61	Rice noodle, fresh, boiled/reheated	40
Idaho potatoes, boiled or microwaved	76*	Sweet potato, oven-baked	46
Jasmine rice, boiled	85*	Basmati rice, boiled	58
Couscous	65*	Barley, pearled, boiled	25*
Orange drink, regular, ready-to-drink	66	Orange juice, unsweetened	50*

* average GI value of different varieties tested

GI data sourced from:
The New Glucose Revolution—complete guide to GI values, *by J Brand-Miller,*
K Foster-Powell & S Holt, Hodder Headline: Sydney, Australia, 2003, and
The Low GI Diet *by J Brand-Miller, K Foster-Powell & J McMillan Price,*
Hodder Headline: Sydney, Australia, 2004.

reference food. The final GI value for the test food is the average GI value for the food in the group of people studied.

Different people produce different blood glucose responses to the same food due to differences in their body size, genetics and lifestyle factors. The use of the reference food to calculate GI values helps reduce the effect of these natural differences between people. Glucose sugar is used as the reference food because it produces a very high blood glucose response.

The GI compares the blood glucose responses produced by different foods and drinks on the same relative basis: the GI value of glucose is set at 100 and the GI values of all other foods and drinks are scored relative to that. Currently, scientists classify foods that produce GI values of 55 or less as low-GI foods. Foods that produce GI values of 56–69 are medium-GI foods, and foods with GI values of 70 or more are high-GI foods.

why can't I find GI values for some foods and drinks?

GI values can only be measured for foods and drinks that contain substantial amounts of digestible carbohydrate. Some foods and drinks, such as meat, fish, poultry, eggs, certain nuts and vegetables, butter, sour cream and diet soft drinks, contain very little, if any, carbohydrate and won't raise your blood glucose level. Therefore it's not possible to measure a GI value for these foods, but they can be considered to be low glycemic.

GI VALUE FOR TEST FOOD

% total 2 hour blood glucose response for test food
_____
% total 2 hour blood glucose response for equal-carbohydrate portion of reference food

Although many products have had their GI values measured, not all of these GI values have been published and many other carbohydrate-containing foods and drinks still need to be tested. GI testing takes time and money, and new GI values will continue to be published in the future.* However, if you want to find out the GI value of a product, call the manufacturer and encourage them to have the product's GI value measured if they haven't already done so.

which factors determine a food's GI value?

The GI value of food or drink is mostly determined by the rate at which its carbohydrate is digested. High-GI foods and drinks contain rapidly digested carbohydrate that produces a fast, large rise in blood glucose and insulin levels. Low-GI foods and drinks contain carbohydrate that is either digested at a slower rate, producing a lower rise in blood glucose and insulin, or they

* *Refer to www.glycemicindex.com for new GI values.*

contain a lot of fructose sugar, which doesn't cause a marked rise in blood glucose or insulin. Carbohydrate digestion is influenced by a number of factors, which is why a food's GI value cannot always be predicted from its nutrient content or ingredients.

what factors affect the rate at which carbohydrate is digested?

the type and amount of starch: There are two main types of digestible starches found in foods—amylose and amylopectin. Amylose is digested at a slower rate than amylopectin. Starchy foods that contain a greater proportion of amylose have a lower GI value than similar foods that contain a greater amount of amylopectin. For example, basmati rice is lower in GI value than jasmine rice because it contains more amylose starch.

the type and amount of sugar: Sugars vary in their GI values. Glucose and sucrose (regular household sugar) and other sugar-based ingredients used in processed foods (corn syrup, maltodextrins) have relatively high-GI values, whereas lactose (milk sugar) and fructose (fruit sugar) have low-GI values. Low-calorie sugar substitutes, such as sucralose, do not increase blood glucose and insulin levels, and can be used to lower both the calorie content and glycemic effect of foods and drinks.

food processing: Whole grains contain a fibrous outer layer that acts as a barrier, increasing the time it takes for the body's digestive enzymes to reach the starch inside the grain. When whole grains are progressively refined from cracked grains into flour, their starch becomes easier to digest and their GI value increases. White or whole wheat (wholemeal) bread has a high GI value, whereas bread with whole or cracked grains has a lower GI value. Similarly, bread made from coarse stone-ground flour has a lower GI value than bread made from regular fine flour, because its larger starch particles take a little longer to digest. Processed quick-cooking oats also have a higher GI value than traditional slow-cooking wholegrain oats. Certain food processing methods, such as puffing and flaking grains makes the starch in the grains much more digestible and increases their GI. Therefore, in general the less processed a grain product (and more grainy), the lower its GI value.

cooking time: Soaking time affects the GI value of many starchy foods. Overcooked pasta has a higher GI value than *al dente* pasta, because its starch is more easily digested. Noodles are also affected in this way.

the type and amount of fiber: If present in large enough amounts and not too refined, soluble fibers can work to slow down the rate of food digestion by making digested food in the stomach more viscous (sticky). Psyllium fiber, consumed as a supplement or added to foods is a good source of soluble fiber, as are legumes (lentils, beans, chickpeas), barley and wholegrain rolled oats.

fat: Due to its high calorie content, fat can slow down the rate of food digestion in the stomach. Foods that contain carbohydrate and a significant amount of fat (e.g. chocolate, premium ice creams, tortilla chips, pizza, potato chips) generally have low-GI values, however these foods should not be a regular part of a healthy diet because of their high fat content.

protein: Protein can entrap particles of starch in certain foods, which makes it harder for digestive enzymes to reach this starch and slows the rate of starch digestion. This is one reason why durum wheat pasta, grainy breads and legumes have low-GI values.

organic acids and other compounds: A certain amount of acid can lower a food's GI value by decreasing the rate or amount of carbohydrate digestion (e.g. acids in sourdough breads, vinegar eaten with starchy foods). Certain compounds that naturally occur in some foods can also decrease starch digestion (e.g. antinutrients in legumes).

who can benefit from a healthy, low-GI diet?

When you consider how many times you eat and drink each day and the big metabolic changes these meals cause on your body, it's not surprising that your dietary habits have a major impact on your health and how you feel during the day. A healthy, varied diet based on low-GI carbohydrate-rich food and drinks will produce lower blood glucose and insulin levels after meals, which is immediately beneficial to people with diabetes and other insulin resistance problems, but also has benefits for everyone: it helps control blood cholesterol and triglyceride levels; it can help control your appetite and body weight; and may even help improve your mental performance. A healthy low-GI diet offers both immediate and long-term health benefits, particularly in conjunction with other healthy lifestyle practices (e.g. regular physical exercise and low to moderate alcohol consumption). During the last 5 years, scientific research has shown that the consumption of a low-GI diet can help reduce your risk of developing many

THE BENEFITS OF LOW-GI DIETS

- *Better blood sugar control*
- *Better blood cholesterol levels*
- *Improved alertness*
- *Improved energy levels*
- *Easier weight control*
- *Reduced risk of heart disease, type 2 diabetes (adult-onset) and certain cancers*

Examples of blood glucose responses to a high- and low-GI meal

This graph depicts the kind of difference in blood glucose levels seen in healthy people after they have eaten equal carbohydrate servings of low-GI and high-GI meals. (People started eating at 0 minutes and finished eating by 15 minutes.)

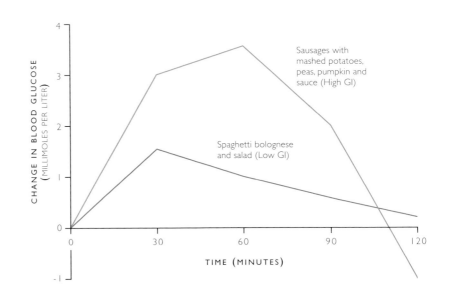

Examples of blood insulin responses to the same high- and low-GI meal

This graph shows the typical difference in blood insulin levels in the same healthy people after consuming the same low-GI and high-GI meals as above. Due to its high glycemic response, the high-GI meal also produces a much higher blood insulin response.

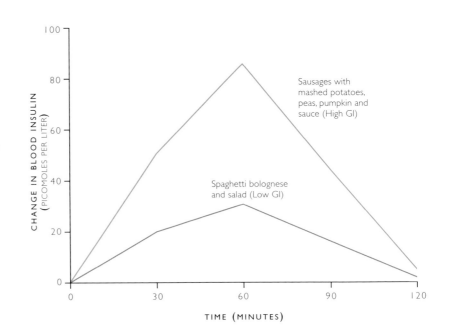

of the serious illnesses that people in industrialized societies typically develop with age: cardiovascular diseases, type 2 (adult-onset) diabetes and certain cancers (bowel, breast, pancreas, uterus).

how does a low-GI diet help make weight control easier?

There are two important ways in which a low-GI diet is beneficial for weight control: it can help control your hunger and calorie intake; and it enables your body to use more fat for fuel. After you eat a high-GI meal, your blood glucose level rises rapidly which causes insulin to be released into your bloodstream. The high insulin response causes your body to store both fat and glucose. This means that the blood levels of the body's two main sources of fuel (glucose and fatty acids) are relatively low 1–2 hours after you eat a high-GI meal. The drop in the blood's fuel levels is thought to cause the brain to trigger the sensation of hunger in order to promote eating and quickly replenish the blood's glucose level (since glucose is the brain's preferred source of fuel).

Unlike high-GI meals, low-GI meals do not produce a dramatic change in blood glucose and insulin levels. Recent scientific studies have shown that diets based on low-GI carbohydrate-rich foods help people lose more body fat than high-GI diets with a similar amount of calories. Low-GI meals enable your body to use more fat for fuel due to the lower insulin responses they produce. Scientific research studies have also shown that both lean and obese people feel less hungry and eat fewer calories at subsequent meals after they are fed low-GI meals instead of similar high-GI meals. The filling effect is particularly powerful when low-GI meals contain a combination of slowly digested starch, fiber and protein (e.g. basmati rice with lentils or spaghetti bolognese)—a combination that slows down the rate of food digestion and therefore the rate at which hunger returns.

low-GI diets can help control your appetite

Hunger, boredom and a sense of deprivation are common problems that stop people from sticking with a weight control diet. The good news about low-GI eating is that it can help you eat less calories while still eating regular, satisfying meals, making it easier for you to adopt this style of eating for life. You don't need to cut all of your favorite foods from your diet. You just need to focus on eating low-GI carbohydrate-rich foods and a balanced variety of nutritious foods most of the time. Wholesome low-GI foods, such as grainy bread, wholegrain cereal products, brown pasta and whole apples, are more

A low-GI diet can offer health benefits for everyone. Basing your meals on low-GI foods will prevent large rises and falls in your blood sugar and insulin levels throughout the day. This type of metabolic response has a number of benefits: it can help you feel more alert and energetic throughout the day; it slows the rate at which hunger returns after meals; it reduces the body's use of antioxidants; and it enables the body to use more fat for fuel.

difficult to over-eat than their more refined counterparts, such as white bread, white pasta, cereal flakes and fruit juice. Adding legumes (e.g. lentils, chickpeas, soy beans, kidney beans) to salads, soups, stews, rice and pasta sauce, or barley to rice are also good ways to boost the filling power of your meals, so you don't need to eat a second helping.

low-GI diets and cardiovascular disease

Scientific research studies conducted over the last 20 years in which people have been placed on high- or low-GI diets have shown that high-GI diets increase inflammation and produce undesirable changes in blood fats that increase the risk of heart disease (higher triglycerides and lower "good" high density protein (HDL)-cholesterol). Other studies that have followed the dietary habits and health status of large numbers of people over time have found that high-GI diets are associated with an increased risk of coronary heart disease and heart attacks. This is partly due to the adverse metabolic effects resulting from chronic high blood glucose and insulin levels, including increased blood pressure and blood coagulation. High-GI diets may also increase the risk of stroke by increasing the body's use of antioxidants, and aggravating blood pressure and blood-flow problems. Reducing the GI of your diet is an easy thing you can do to lower your risk of cardiovascular disease while also adopting other healthy lifestyle practices, such as getting regular physical exercise, reducing your saturated fat intake, maintaining a healthy body weight and not smoking.

low-GI diets for the prevention and treatment of type 2 diabetes

Diabetes mellitus is a condition in which a person's blood glucose level is abnormally high either because their body can't make enough insulin (type 1 diabetes) or their body is resistant to the effects of insulin (type 2 diabetes). If left untreated, diabetes greatly increases the risk of many health problems, including heart disease, blindness and kidney failure. Type 2 diabetes is the most common form and typically develops in people aged over 40, although more and more people are developing the condition at an earlier age. The risk of developing insulin resistance and type 2 diabetes is increased by: being overweight and inactive; having a family history of diabetes; developing diabetes during pregnancy; eating too much saturated fat; and eating a high-GI diet. The long-term consumption of a high-GI diet increases the risk of developing insulin resistance and type 2 diabetes by enhancing body fat storage and by over-taxing the body's ability to produce sufficient insulin.

A healthy low-GI diet together with regular exercise can reduce your risk of developing type 2 diabetes by helping you control your weight and by improving your body's insulin sensitivity (less insulin is required by the body to metabolise nutrients). A healthy diet and regular exercise are two relatively simple things to do, but you need to make a focused effort to achieve them, because our modern lifestyle makes it very easy for us to overeat and be inactive. If you already have type 2 diabetes, then a low-GI diet can help you control your blood sugar level and your blood triglyceride and cholesterol levels. See a qualified dietitian for advice about planning low-GI meals and snacks around your daily medication and activity schedule.

healthy eating the low-GI way

Advances in scientific research have recently led health authorities to change the amounts of fat, protein and carbohydrate they recommend for a healthy diet. It is now known that the emphasis should not be on eating low-fat foods (which was the trend in the past), but rather, on eating a healthy balance of good quality fats (that is, low saturated fat intake plus sufficient

TIPS FOR SWITCHING FROM HIGH- TO LOW-GI MEALS

MEAL	HIGHER GI MENU	LOWER GI VERSION
Breakfast	1 bowl of cereal flakes with milk and 2 teaspoons of sugar 2 slices white toast with strawberry jam Tea with milk	1 bowl of natural granola with milk and fresh pear slices 1 slice wholegrain toast with pure fruit spread (no added sugar) Tea with milk
Snack	Small carton of regular flavored milk Iced cupcake	Small carton of flavored milk with sugar substitute 1 nectarine or apple
Lunch	Ham and salad on a white bread roll Can of soft drink	Ham and salad on a wholegrain roll Small bottle of unsweetened apple juice
Dinner	Stir-fried beef and vegetables with 1.5 cups of jasmine rice Canned fruit salad in heavy syrup with ice cream	Stir-fried beef and vegetables with 1 cup of basmati rice (extra serve of vegetables, not rice, if you want more) Fresh or canned peach slices in juice with ice cream

If you have always eaten white bread and find it difficult to switch to wholegrain, try to make this change in a series of steps. For example, switch to whole wheat (wholemeal) bread first, then gradually start eating breads with cracked and whole grains in them. Alternatively, if you don't like grainy bread, stick with your preferred bread and make other changes to lower the overall GI of your diet, such as switching to a lower GI rice and breakfast cereal, and low-GI fruit.

omega-3 fatty acids and monounsaturated fats) and mostly choosing healthier low-GI carbohydrate-rich foods.

Typically, in the past when people adopted low-fat diets, they also increased their intake of high-GI carbohydrates. This often prevented people from lowering their body weight and blood cholesterol level. We now know that the quantity and quality of both dietary fat and carbohydrate are important for good health and weight control. Consequently, health authorities, such as the World Health Organization, now recommend that people reduce both the saturated fat content and the GI of their diet.

Health authorities have developed healthy eating guidelines and the healthy diet pyramid to help people work out the types and amounts of foods they should be eating for good health. Food pyramids are a basic guide to show the general proportions of the different food groups people should eat for long-term good health. Depending on your individual health needs and food preferences, it's now recommended that your daily energy (calorie) intake consists of 45–65% from carbohydrate; 25–35% from protein; and 15–35% from fat. While the absolute amounts of each nutrient may vary between people, the guidelines about which foods should feature more often than others in a healthy diet are the same for everyone and

TRADITIONAL FOOD PYRAMID   LOW-GI FOOD PYRAMID

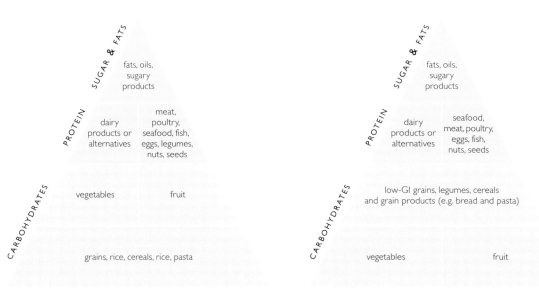

This picture shows how easy it can be to lower the GI of your diet by making simple substitutions such as swapping white bread with whole-grain bread, switching from cereal flakes to granola, and replacing sugar with naturally sweet fresh fruit on top of your breakfast cereal.

are best represented by the healthy diet pyramid. The healthy diet pyramid shows you how to eat a balanced diet by selecting a variety of foods from each of the main food groups each day, with main meals and snacks consisting mostly of fruit, vegetables, legumes and grain products (preferably low GI).

how can I lower the GI of my diet?

The diet pyramid is a useful guide to show you the amounts of different foods you should consume. In order to reduce the overall GI of your diet, you need to first identify the foods that provide you with most of your carbohydrate (e.g. bread, breakfast cereals, rice, potatoes, pasta, fruit juice, bananas, soft drinks, pizza, chips, cakes, muffins, cookies, confectionery and snack foods) then aim to eat lower GI versions or alternatives of these products most of the time. This can substantially lower the GI of your diet.

You don't need to totally ban high- or medium-GI foods from your diet. Just make sure that you don't eat them as often as low-GI foods. (Many low-GI starchy foods are relatively high in fiber or bulky, so you may need to gradually increase your intake.)

In addition to being more selective about food choice, you may also need to look at your cooking methods. Make sure that you don't cook pasta, rice or potatoes until they are very soft and soggy. Pasta should be served *al dente*, as its GI value will increase the longer it is cooked. Eat whole potatoes and whole fruit rather than mashed potatoes and fruit juice. Another good way to lower the GI of a high-GI food, such as calrose rice, is

to dilute it with a low-GI food, such as barley or lentils. Instead of eating a cup of rice, you can eat half a cup of rice and half a cup of barley or lentils. This is also more filling and has a lower GI than the rice alone.

why not cut out carbohydrates instead?

Instead of choosing low-GI versions of carbohydrate-rich foods, another way of lowering the total blood sugar effect (the glycemic impact or glycemic load) of your diet is to significantly reduce your carbohydrate intake. In fact, the aim of high-protein diets that have recently become popular again is to lower your carbohydrate intake in order to make your body secrete less insulin. However, there are potential problems associated with the low-carb approach: it can increase your saturated fat intake; it reduces your intake of many important nutrients; it requires considerable effort to purchase and prepare suitable foods; it's difficult to maintain over a long period of time; it can make you feel tired and irritable; and it has not been proven to be safe in the long term. A healthy diet based on the low-GI diet pyramid together with regular exercise is an easier and scientifically-proven method of controlling your insulin levels and body weight and is recommended by health authorities, such as the World Health Organization.

dietary fat—getting the balance right

Along with low-GI carbohydrates, a healthy diet also requires a good balance of dietary fat in order to reduce your risk of developing diabetes and heart disease. To achieve this, you need to limit both your total fat intake and saturated fat intake. You don't need to aim for a very low-fat diet, but you do need to focus on obtaining your dietary fat from healthier foods rather than "junk" foods. Limiting your fat intake is also important if you're trying to control your weight, because fatty foods are rich in calories but are less filling than foods rich in protein or carbohydrate. So fatty foods make it easy for you to eat more calories than you need.

The fat in foods is a mixture of three different types of fat: saturated, monounsaturated and polyunsaturated. There are two types of polyunsaturated fats: omega-6 and omega-3 fats. Different foods vary in the amounts of the three types of fat they contain. When eaten as part of a diet that is relatively low in total and saturated fat, polyunsaturated and monounsaturated fats can help lower your blood cholesterol level. However, a lower fat diet that contains a lot more omega-6 fat than omega-3 fat can enhance insulin resistance and lower the level of "good" HDL-cholesterol in the blood, particularly in combination with high-GI foods.

Foods rich in omega-6 fat include most nuts, seeds and plant oils (e.g. sunflower, safflower, corn, sesame, peanut and soy bean oils). Good sources of omega-3 fats include oily fish (e.g. mackerel, Atlantic salmon, tuna, herring, rainbow trout, anchovies, sea perch and mullet), octopus, rock oysters, omega-3 enriched eggs, flaxseeds (linseeds), flaxseed oil, canola oil, walnuts and walnut oil. Due to the widespread consumption of margarines, cooking oils and processed foods, typical western diets contain 10–20 times more omega-6 fat than omega-3 fat whereas the ideal ratio is equal amounts of both types of these fats. Most people in western countries can greatly reduce their risk of developing many serious illnesses by making dietary changes to reduce the GI and saturated fat content of their diet while increasing the proportion of monounsaturated and omega-3 fats they consume. Use canola and olive oil-based margarines and mayonnaise and cook with canola or olive oil.

portion control

If you're still having trouble losing weight after reducing your fat intake and switching to low-GI carbohydrate-rich foods, then you need to determine whether you're still eating too much food for the amount of physical activity you do. If this is difficult, consult a dietitian who can determine whether you are overeating certain foods. It can be easy to consume more carbohydrate than you need if you regularly drink lots of soft drinks or fruit juice and eat large portions of pasta and rice (more than 1.5–2 cups cooked pasta or rice per meal). Between-meal snacks, rich in fat and/or carbohydrate, can also be a source of unnecessary calories if eaten on a regular basis (e.g. chips and cookies). Following the dietary pyramid model can help with portion control. Base your main meals around a low-GI grain, legumes or grain product plus vegetables or fruit, then add some lean protein and healthy fat. This means that the greatest quantity of food you consume at each meal is in the form of vegetables and/or fruit and the low-GI carbohydrate-rich food. If you feel like more food, eat some more low-carbohydrate vegetables or fruit.

what is the glycemic load?

GI values are measured using portions of foods that contain a fixed amount of digestible carbohydrate (usually 1¾ oz/50 grams). In everyday life people eat different size portions of the same foods at various times. Consequently, the glycemic load (GL) concept was developed to estimate the total glycemic (blood sugar) effects produced by realistic meals and snacks containing different amounts of carbohydrate.

GL CATEGORIES

MEALS AND SNACKS
- *Low GL ≤ 10*
- *Medium GL 11–19*
- *High GL ≥ 20*

TOTAL DAY'S GL
- *Low GL < 80*
- *High GL > 120*

TYPE OF FOOD	HIGHER GI VERSIONS	LOWER GI ALTERNATIVES
Bread	Regular soft textured white, whole wheat or rye bread and bread rolls, white or whole wheat bagels, gluten-free bread, lebanese bread, melba toast, biscuits	Wholegrain breads with a relatively dense texture, pumpernickel bread, pita bread, sourdough bread, breads made from coarse stoneground flour
Grains	Most types of rice (especially jasmine), millet; polenta (cornmeal)	Basmati rice, wild rice, pearled barley, quinoa, buckwheat, bulghur wheat (cracked wheat)
Pasta and noodles	Gluten-free corn or rice pasta, low-fat instant noodles, dried rice noodles, udon noodles, couscous	Durum wheat pasta—regular or protein-enriched, gluten-free legume-based pasta, mung bean noodles, fresh rice noodles, soba (buckwheat) noodles, tortellini, ravioli
Breakfast cereals	Most processed breakfast cereals, including puffed grains (rice, amaranth, wheat, buckwheat), instant oatmeal, regular wheat breakfast cereals	Semolina, oatmeal made from whole or steel-cut oats, oat bran, natural granola (without flakes), oat bran wheat cookies
Cookies and crackers *	Puffed crispbreads, water crackers, wafer cookies, plain sweet cookies: oatmeal cookies	Cookies made with stoneground flour, whole rolled oats or whole grains with low GI dried fruit
Vegetables and legumes **	Squash, parsnips, rutabaga, tapioca; most potatoes—steamed, boiled, mashed (new potatoes have the lowest GI value out of the common varieties tested so far, but are still medium GI)	Sweet potato, yams, taro, green peas, carrots, sweet corn, all legumes (dried, boiled, canned, vacuum-packed); non-starchy vegetables (e.g. onions, tomatoes, lettuce, mushrooms, artichokes, asparagus, broccoli, cauliflower, ginger, garlic, cucumber, celery, pepper, leek, arugula), herbs
Fruit	Canteloupe, watermelon, sweetened dried cranberries, raisins, dried tenderized figs, lychees, canned in syrup, dark cherries, breadfruit, papaya	Apples, pears, stone fruit (raw or canned in natural juice), berries, bananas (the less ripe, the lower the GI), prunes, dried apples, apricots, peaches, pears, golden raisins, kiwi fruit, mango, custard apple, citrus fruit, grapes
Dairy products and alternatives ***	Rice milk, sweetened condensed milk	Cows' milk—plain or flavored, all types, soy milk—plain or flavored, all types, yogurt, ice cream, custard pudding, fromage frais, diet gelatin dessert

* Some cookies and crackers have low-GI values due to their high fat content, and should not be eaten regularly.

** Most vegetables and herbs contain a little carbohydrate and don't produce a marked rise in blood glucose.

*** Dairy products that are sweetened with sugar have a higher GI value than those sweetened with a low-calorie sugar substitute.

GL values are calculated for a particular serving of a food by multiplying the GI value of the food by the amount of digestible carbohydrate in that portion of the food. For example, a small serve of cooked basmati rice contains 42 grams of digestible carbohydrate and has a GI of 58. Therefore, the GL for this portion of rice is $(42 \times 58)/100 = 24$. However, if the same weight of jasmine rice had been chosen instead of basmati rice (carbohydrate content of 42 grams and GI of 109), then the GL of the portion of rice consumed would be 46, almost twice as high. To avoid getting confused by lots of numbers and calculations, you can make the GI concept work for you by simply focusing on choosing lower-GI foods instead of high-GI carbohydrate-rich foods—most of the time. The GL is a useful thing for scientists to consider, but it's not necessary for everyone to use. If you simply swap the higher GI foods in your diet with similar amounts of lower GI versions, you'll automatically reduce the overall GI of your diet.

about the recipes in this book

The aim of this book is to provide you with valid information about the GI values of foods and the importance of a healthy low-GI diet for maintaining good health. The GI values of foods are based on their blood sugar responses and are immediately relevant for people with diabetes, but they are also relevant to anyone who wants to improve their health and their mental and physical performance. It also provides you with practical tips to show you how easy it is to make low-GI foods a regular feature of your diet.

The recipes give you a huge range of delicious tested options for both everyday eating and special occasions. They are all low-GI and have been chosen to meet other healthy eating goals as well, including healthy fat and fiber levels. Underneath each recipe, you will find the approximate nutrient content of an average serve of the finished dish plus its estimated GI category. These were calculated by an experienced dietitian using published GI values for the carbohydrate-containing ingredients. If a published GI value wasn't available for a particular ingredient, then the GI value of a similar alternative or an estimated GI value was used. Due to the use of estimated GI values for some ingredients and the unpredictable effects of certain cooking methods and food combinations, the GI ratings are estimates only. However, it is expected that in most cases, the low-GI category will be correct because low-GI ingredients feature in these recipes. Nonetheless, it would be useful for people with diabetes to monitor their individual blood glucose responses to the recipes in this book, in order to establish which dishes enable them to control their blood glucose level most effectively.

Low-GI, fiber-rich breakfasts are a great way to make you alert and give you plenty of energy to start the day. They are also very good for weight control because they keep you feeling full for hours. Scientific research has shown that children and adults who eat a carbohydrate-rich breakfast score higher in memory and concentration tests than those who skip breakfast or eat a fatty meal.

breakfast

banana smoothie

This calcium-rich smoothie is good for your teeth and bones and makes a delicious light breakfast or energy boost between meals.

2 just-ripe bananas

¼ cup (2¼ oz/60 g) low-fat vanilla or fruit-flavored yogurt

2 cups (17 fl oz/500 ml) low-fat milk (or soy milk)

2 tbs wheat germ

freshly grated nutmeg, to taste

Prep time: 5 minutes

Cooking time: 0

Serves 2

Put the bananas in a blender or food processor. Add the yogurt, milk, wheat germ and nutmeg.

Blend or process until smooth, then pour into two chilled glasses.

HINTS: The GI of bananas increases as the fruit ripens so choose bananas that have only just ripened.

You can substitute the bananas with other low-GI fruit, such as berries, pears, apricots, plums, peaches or nectarines.

nutrition per serving Energy 248 Cal (1041 kJ); Fat 1.3 g; Saturated fat 0.5 g; Protein 16.9 g; Carbohydrate 43 g; Fiber 3.4 g; Cholesterol 12 mg

breakfast smoothie

This refreshing smoothie provides carbohydrate and protein to help energize your brain and body and improve your mood. It's very easy to put together and even easier to drink.

5½ oz (150 g) fresh low-GI fruit (e.g. peaches, plums, nectarines, apricots, pears, apples or any type of berry)

¼ cup (2¼ oz/60 g) low-fat vanilla yogurt

I cup (9 fl oz/250 ml) low-fat milk (or soy milk)

I tbs malted milk powder

2 tsp wheat germ

I egg (optional)

Prep time: 5 minutes
Cooking time: 0
Serves 2

Put the fruit in a blender or food processor. Add the yogurt, milk, milk powder, wheat germ and egg (if you are using it).

Blend or process until well combined, then pour into two chilled glasses.

HINTS: Experiment with various low-GI fruits to work out your favorite combination for this low-fat smoothie.

There are many types and flavors of yogurt on the market. If you are trying to control your weight and/or your blood sugar level, choose diet yogurt that contains a low-calorie sweetener instead of sugar. This will add more sweetness and flavor to the smoothie but won't increase the GI.

Diet yogurt that is sweetened with aspartame or a similar low-calorie sweetener has a lower GI and less calories than yogurt sweetened with sugar, but the sugar-sweetened yogurt is still low-GI.

nutrition per serving Energy 121 Cal (508 kJ); Fat 1.8 g; Saturated fat 0.7 g; Protein 9.9 g; Carbohydrate 16.1 g; Fiber 1.8 g; Cholesterol 53 mg

poached eggs with spinach and garlic yogurt dressing

This easy recipe gives you a new twist on poached eggs with more nutrients and flavor and far less fat than eggs benedict. It's an ideal meal to enjoy with friends on lazy weekends.

DRESSING
½ cup (4½ oz/125 g) low-fat plain yogurt
1 small garlic clove, crushed
1 tbs chopped chives

10½ oz (300 g) baby spinach leaves
½ oz (15 g) canola or olive oil margarine
4 tomatoes, halved
1 tbs white vinegar
8 eggs
8 thick slices wholegrain bread, toasted

Prep time: 10 minutes
Cooking time: 15 minutes
Serves 4

To make the dressing, mix together the yogurt, garlic and chives.

Wash the spinach and put it in a large saucepan with just the little water that is left clinging to the leaves. Cover the pan and cook over low heat for 3–4 minutes, or until the spinach has wilted. Add the margarine, then season with salt and freshly ground black pepper and toss together. Remove the pan from the heat and keep warm.

Put the tomatoes, cut side up, under a preheated broiler (grill) and cook for 3–5 minutes, or until softened and warm.

Fill a deep frying pan three-quarters full with cold water and add the vinegar and some salt to stop the egg whites spreading. Bring the water to a gentle simmer. Gently break an egg into a small bowl, then carefully slide into the water, then repeat with the remaining eggs. Reduce the heat so that the water barely moves. Cook for 1–2 minutes, or until the eggs are just set. Remove with a spatula. Drain on paper towels.

Top each slice of toast with some spinach, an egg and some dressing. Serve with tomato halves.

nutrition per serving Energy 422 Cal (1772 kJ); Fat 16.1 g; Saturated fat 5.4 g; Protein 26.1 g; Carbohydrate 42.5 g; Fiber 8.3 g; Cholesterol 386 mg

lamb's liver and bacon

A highly nutritious meal that's great for breakfast or brunch, particularly in cold weather. It is rich in vitamin A, iron, zinc and folate.

1 lb 2 oz (500 g) lamb's liver

all-purpose (plain) flour, to dust

1½ cups (13 fl oz/375 ml) chicken stock

1 tsp worcestershire sauce

½ oz (15 g) reduced-fat canola or olive oil margarine

2 tsp canola or olive oil

2 onions, sliced

8 slices low-fat bacon (we used 97% fat-free), chopped

canola or olive oil spray

2 tbs chopped parsley

4 thick slices wholegrain bread, toasted

Prep time: 20 minutes

Cooking time: 15 minutes

Serves 4

Peel off and discard the outer membrane from the lamb's liver, then cut the flesh into ½ in (1 cm) slices. Put some flour in a shallow bowl and season with salt and freshly ground black pepper. Dust the lamb's liver with the seasoned flour and shake off the excess flour, reserving 2 tablespoons.

Blend the chicken stock, worcestershire sauce and reserved flour in a pitcher.

Heat the margarine and oil in a frying pan over medium heat, add the onion and cook for 3 minutes, or until golden. Remove the onion from the pan and set aside. Add the bacon to the pan and cook over medium heat for 2 minutes, or until brown. Remove from the pan and set aside.

Spray the pan with oil. Add the lamb's liver to the pan and cook over high heat for 1 minute on each side, or until lightly browned. Return the onion to the pan, then pour in the chicken stock mixture and stir until the mixture boils and thickens. Reduce the heat to low and simmer for 3 minutes, or until the lamb's liver is tender. Stir in the cooked bacon and parsley. Serve immediately with the toast.

HINT: Lamb's liver should be pink in the center when cooked—do not be tempted to overcook it or it will become tough.

The coarser the bread and the more whole grains it contains, the lower the GI. Any type of bread with whole or cracked grains will generally have a lower GI than white or whole wheat (wholemeal) bread.

nutrition per serving Energy 378 Cal (1583 kJ); Fat 17.3 g; Saturated fat 4.4 g; Protein 43.1 g; Carbohydrate 27 g; Fiber 2.9 g; Cholesterol 550 mg

herb omelette

This nourishing omelette is ready in a flash and is delicious at any time of the day. The combination of protein and low-GI carbohydrate is very sustaining.

4 eggs
2 tbs finely chopped parsley
2 tbs chopped chives
canola or olive oil spray
⅓ cup (1½ oz/40 g) low-fat grated Cheddar cheese
4 thick slices wholegrain bread, toasted

Prep time: 10 minutes
Cooking time: 5 minutes
Serves 2

Break the eggs into a large bowl and whisk with a fork. Whisk in 2 tablespoons of water, then add the parsley and chives. Season with salt and freshly ground black pepper.

Spray a small non-stick frying pan with oil. Heat over high heat, then reduce the heat and add half of the omelette mixture. Swirl with a fork several times.

While the mixture is cooking, tilt the pan and lift the edge of the omelette occasionally to allow the uncooked egg to flow underneath. When the mixture is half cooked, sprinkle with half of the grated cheese, then leave to cook a little more (the base should be golden brown and the inside nearly set). Using a spatula, fold the omelette in half in the pan. Flip it over onto a warm plate.

Gently re-whisk the remaining egg mixture, then cook in the same way as the first. Serve with the toast.

nutrition per serving Energy 407 Cal (1708 kJ); Fat 16.5 g; Saturated fat 4.7 g; Protein 27.7 g; Carbohydrate 37.1g; Fiber 4.5 g; Cholesterol 382 mg

scrambled eggs with broiled tomatoes and mushrooms

Scrambled eggs and wholegrain toast make for a nourishing breakfast. Mushrooms and tomatoes add flavor and nutrients to make this a guaranteed crowd pleaser.

2 vine-ripened tomatoes, halved

4 large mushrooms

canola or olive oil spray

2 tsp thyme, plus extra to garnish

6 eggs

1 tbs reduced-fat milk

1 oz (30 g) reduced-fat canola or olive oil margarine

4 slices wholegrain bread, toasted

Prep time: 5 minutes
Cooking time: 10 minutes
Serves 2

Put the tomatoes (cut side up) and mushrooms under a preheated broiler (grill), then spray with oil and sprinkle with the thyme leaves. Cook for 3–5 minutes, or until warmed.

Meanwhile, break the eggs into a bowl, add the milk and season well with salt and freshly ground black pepper. Whisk gently with a fork until well combined.

Melt half the margarine in a small non-stick saucepan or frying pan over low heat. Add the eggs, then stir constantly with a wooden spoon. Do not turn up the heat—scrambling must be done slowly and gently. When most of the egg has set, add the remaining margarine and remove the pan from the heat. There should be enough heat left in the pan to finish cooking the eggs and melt the margarine. Serve immediately on toast. Arrange the tomatoes and mushrooms on the side. Garnish with extra thyme leaves.

HINT: It is very important to use fresh eggs when scrambling. To check whether an egg is fresh put it in a bowl of cold water. If it sinks on its side it is fresh, if it floats on its end it is stale. If it is somewhere between the two it is not perfectly fresh but still good enough to use.

nutrition per serving Energy 550 Cal (2303 kJ); Fat 29.3 g; Saturated fat 6.8 g; Protein 30.5 g; Carbohydrate 41.4 g; Fiber 7.1 g; Cholesterol 563 mg

swiss granola

Running out of time in the morning is no excuse for missing out on the benefits of a healthy breakfast. This satisfying granola takes only 10 minutes to prepare, and you can make it in the evening and then enjoy it the next morning.

1 apple, cored but not peeled

½ cup (4½ oz/125 g) thick low-fat plain yogurt

2 tbs raw almonds or hazelnuts, chopped

1 cup (3½ oz/100 g) wholegrain rolled oats

Prep time: 10 minutes

Cooking time: 0

Serves 2

Grate the apple, including the skin, into a bowl. Add the yogurt, nuts and oats, then mix well and serve.

HINTS: This granola is delicious served with fresh or canned low-GI fruit such as pears, peaches, nectarines, plums or apricots—choose fruit canned in natural juice rather than syrup.

If the granola isn't moist enough for you, add some unsweetened apple juice or milk to it before serving.

To add some omega-3 essential fat to your diet, add 1–2 tablespoons ground flaxseeds (linseeds) to the granola.

nutrition per serving Energy 315 Cal (1325 kJ); Fat 10.7 g; Saturated fat 1.1 g; Protein 10.9 g; Carbohydrate 43.7 g; Fiber 6 g; Cholesterol 3 mg

home-made granola

Being based on a variety of healthy ingredients, granola provides a healthy mix of nutrients and delicious flavors. Served with fresh fruit, milk or yogurt it's a great way to start the day.

2 cups (7 oz/200 g) wholegrain rolled oats (or wholegrain rolled barley)

2 tbs wheat germ

¼ cup (¾ oz/20 g) unprocessed wheat bran

½ cup (3¼ oz/90 g) dried apricots, chopped

½ cup (1¼ oz/35 g) dried apple, chopped

⅓ cup (1½ oz/40 g) golden raisins (sultanas)

½ cup (2¼ oz/60 g) slivered raw almonds

low-fat milk or soy milk, to serve

Prep time: 10 minutes
Cooking time: 0
Serves 8

Combine the rolled oats, wheat germ, wheat bran, dried fruit and almonds in a bowl and mix well. Keep in an airtight container for up to 4 weeks.

Serve the granola with low-fat milk or soy milk.

HINTS: You can substitute the almonds with Brazil nuts, hazelnuts or pecans.

To save preparation time, you can buy a packet of chopped dried fruit medley to use instead of the apricot, apple and golden raisins.

For some low-GI serving suggestions, try low-fat yogurt or fresh low-GI fruit, such as berries, apple, pear, peach, plum, apricot or nectarine.

nutrition per serving Energy 191 Cal (803 kJ); Fat 6.2 g; Saturated fat 0.6 g; Protein 5.4 g; Carbohydrate 28.8 g; Fiber 5.1 g; Cholesterol 0 mg

oatmeal

Oatmeal is a sustaining breakfast and especially nice to warm you up on cold winter's mornings. Use traditional slow-cooking oats instead of instant or quick-cooking oats to keep this oatmeal in the low-GI range.

I cup (3½ oz/100 g) wholegrain rolled oats (or rolled barley)

½ cup (4 fl oz/125 ml) low-fat milk, plus extra to serve

Prep time: 5 minutes
Cooking time: 10 minutes
Serves 2

Mix the oats with 1½ cups (13 fl oz/375 ml) cold water in a small heavy-based pan. Stir in the milk and bring to a boil. Cook for about 7 minutes, stirring constantly until thick and creamy. Serve immediately.

Serve the oatmeal with low-fat milk. It is delicious with a dried fruit compote (see recipe on page 41).

HINTS: Health food shops stock wholegrain oats such as Scotch oats and steel-cut oats.

Try making this oatmeal with wholegrain rolled barley for a fiber-rich meal.

For a delicious fruity oatmeal, stir 2 tablespoons of chopped dried apricots into the mixture for the last 3 minutes of cooking. Some other low-GI serving suggestions to try are stewed apple, grated pear or apple, wheat germ, dried apricots, dried apples, prunes or low-fat yogurt.

The coarser the oats, the lower the GI. When choosing oats, avoid instant or "quick-cooking" oats—these are not low GI. Choose the traditional slow-cooking oats instead. If you can't find wholegrain oats in the supermarket, look for them in your healthfood store.

nutrition per serving Energy 207 Cal (868 kJ); Fat 4.3 g; Saturated fat 0.8 g; Protein 7.7 g; Carbohydrate 34.1 g; Fiber 3.4 g; Cholesterol 2 mg

mixed berry couscous

Full of antioxidants and flavor, this tangy dish is a colorful alternative to breakfast cereal and oatmeal.

1 cup (6½ oz/185 g) instant couscous

2 cups (17 fl oz/500 ml) unsweetened apple and blackcurrant juice

1 cinnamon stick

2 tsp orange zest

2 cups (9 oz/250 g) fresh raspberries

1⅔ cups (9 oz/250 g) fresh blueberries

1⅔ cups (9 oz/250 g) strawberries, hulled and halved

low-fat honey or fruit-flavored yogurt, to serve

mint leaves, to garnish

Prep time: 15 minutes

Cooking time: 5 minutes

Serves 4

Put the couscous in a bowl. Pour the apple and blackcurrant juice into a saucepan and add the cinnamon stick. Cover and bring to a boil, then remove from the heat and pour over the couscous. Cover the couscous with plastic wrap and leave for about 5 minutes, or until all the liquid has been absorbed. Remove the cinnamon stick from the bowl.

Separate the grains of couscous with a fork, then gently fold in the orange zest and most of the raspberries, blueberries and strawberries. Spoon the couscous mixture into four bowls and sprinkle with the remaining berries. Serve with a generous dollop of the honey or fruit-flavored yogurt. Garnish with fresh mint leaves and serve immediately.

HINT: Couscous, by itself, has a medium GI, but this meal of couscous with berries, yogurt and fruit juice has a low GI. However, if you are watching your weight or blood sugar level, make sure you limit yourself to one serve of this dish.

nutrition per serving Energy 326 Cal (1370 kJ); Fat 0.7 g; Saturated fat 0.1 g; Protein 10.8 g; Carbohydrate 67.6 g; Fiber 6.3 g; Cholesterol 2 mg

dried fruit compote

If you're having trouble eating three serves of fruit each day, this dish will help you get started. It's also rich in carbohydrate, which is great for keeping you alert throughout the morning.

3 cups (14 oz/400 g) dried fruit salad mixture (dried peaches, prunes, pears, apricots, apples and nectarines)

2 cups (17 fl oz/500 ml) freshly squeezed orange juice

1 tsp soft brown sugar

1–2 star anise

1 vanilla bean, halved lengthwise

vanilla or fruit-flavored low-fat yogurt, to serve

Prep time: 10 minutes
Cooking time: 15 minutes
Serves 4

Put the dried fruit salad in a saucepan. Add the orange juice, sugar, star anise and vanilla bean.

Bring slowly to a boil, then reduce the heat, cover and leave to simmer, stirring occasionally, for 15 minutes, or until the fruit is plump and juicy.

Discard the star anise and vanilla bean. Serve the fruit drizzled with the cooking syrup. Add a dollop of low-fat yogurt, if you like.

HINT: For a slightly different flavor, use a cinnamon stick and 2 cloves instead of the star anise and vanilla bean.

See serving suggestion on page 38.

nutrition per serving Energy 295 Cal (1239 kJ); Fat 0.5 g; Saturated fat 0 g; Protein 3.8 g; Carbohydrate 70.8 g; Fiber 7.9 g; Cholesterol 0 mg

citrus summer salad

This refreshing, zesty fruit salad will awaken your senses and give you a healthy boost of antioxidants. Serve with low-fat yogurt for extra protein and calcium.

3 ruby grapefruits

3 large oranges

1 tbs superfine (caster) sugar

1 cinnamon stick

1 tbs mint, chopped

whole mint leaves, to garnish

plain or vanilla low-fat yogurt, to serve

Prep time: 15 minutes

Cooking time: 5 minutes

Serves 4–6

Peel and remove the pith from the grapefruit and oranges. Carefully cut out the segments and mix together in a bowl.

Put the sugar, cinnamon stick and mint in a small saucepan with 3 tablespoons water and stir over low heat until the sugar has dissolved.

Remove the cinnamon stick and mint from the syrup, then drizzle it over the fruit. Garnish with fresh mint leaves and serve with yogurt.

HINTS: Another good combination for a citrus fruit salad is mandarins, tangelos and pomelos when they are in season.

This salad can be kept in the refrigerator for up to 2 days and the flavor will improve as it develops.

nutrition per serving (6) Energy 75 Cal (315 kJ); Fat 0.3 g; Saturated fat 0 g; Protein 2 g; Carbohydrate 15.6 g; Fiber 2.8 g; Cholesterol 0 mg

Soups and salads offer an easy way to combine a variety of healthy ingredients from different food groups, including vegetables, grains and legumes. The recipes in this chapter include a variety of foods with a wide range of healthy nutrients, including antioxidants. Serving a soup or salad with a low-GI bread, such as crusty wholegrain or pumpernickel, can transform a light dish into a filling meal.

soups & salads

vietnamese beef soup

This classic Vietnamese soup is a full meal in a bowl. Protein-rich beef and low-GI rice noodles will satisfy your hunger and a variety of herbs and spices will feed your senses with exotic aromas and flavors.

14 oz (400 g) lean rump steak, trimmed

½ onion

1½ tbs fish sauce

1 star anise

1 cinnamon stick

pinch ground white pepper

6 cups (52 fl oz/1.5 liters) beef stock

10½ oz (300 g) fresh thin rice noodles

3 scallions (spring onions), thinly sliced

1 small handful Vietnamese mint leaves

1 cup (3¼ oz/90 g) bean sprouts, trimmed

1 small onion, halved and thinly sliced

1 small red chili, thinly sliced on the diagonal

lemon wedges, to serve

Prep time: 20 minutes + 40 minutes freezing
Cooking time: 30 minutes
Serves 4

Wrap the steak in plastic wrap and freeze for 40 minutes as this will make it easier to slice.

Meanwhile, put the onion half, fish sauce, star anise, cinnamon stick, white pepper, stock and 2 cups (17 fl oz/500 ml) water in a large saucepan. Bring to a boil, then reduce the heat, cover and simmer for 20 minutes. Discard the onion, star anise and cinnamon stick.

Put the noodles in a large heatproof bowl. Cover with boiling water and soak for 5 minutes, or until softened. Separate gently and drain. Thinly slice the meat across the grain.

Divide the noodles and scallion among four deep bowls. Top with the beef, mint, bean sprouts, thinly sliced onion and chili. Ladle the hot broth over the top and serve with the lemon wedges—the heat of the liquid will cook the beef.

HINT: It is important to use fresh rice noodles to keep this meal in the low-GI range. Dried rice noodles will increase the GI of the recipe.

nutrition per serving Energy 326 Cal (1367 kJ); Fat 6.1 g; Saturated fat 2.4 g; Protein 31.2 g; Carbohydrate 35.9 g; Fiber 2.5 g; Cholesterol 64 mg

bean and sausage soup

Soup is a great way to warm up on a cold winter's night. This one is rich and hearty and will appeal to the whole family.

2 tsp canola or olive oil

4 thin low-fat beef sausages

2 leeks, sliced

1 garlic clove, crushed

1 large carrot, chopped into small cubes

2 celery stalks, sliced

2 tbs all-purpose (plain) flour

2 beef bouillon (stock) cubes, crumbled

½ cup (4 fl oz/125 ml) white wine

1½ cups (4½ oz/125 g) small pasta shells

14 oz (400 g) can three-bean mix, drained and rinsed

1 tsp chopped fresh chili (optional)

Prep time: 25 minutes

Cooking time: 30 minutes

Serves 4–6

Heat the oil in a large heavy-based saucepan and add the sausages. Cook over medium heat for 5 minutes, or until golden, turning regularly. Drain the cooked sausages on paper towels, and then dice.

Add the leek, garlic, carrot and celery to the pan and cook, stirring occasionally, for 2–3 minutes, or until soft.

Add the flour and cook, stirring, for 1 minute. Add the bouillon cube and wine and gradually stir in 8 cups (70 fl oz/2 liters) water. Bring to a boil, then reduce the heat and simmer for 10 minutes.

Add the pasta, beans and chili (if using) to the pan. Increase the heat and cook for 8–10 minutes, or until the pasta is *al dente*. Return the sausage to the soup and season to taste with salt and freshly ground black pepper. Serve with some low-GI wholegrain bread and a mixed salad for a complete meal.

HINT: You can use dried beans, if you prefer. Put them in a large bowl, cover with water and leave to soak overnight. Drain and rinse well, then transfer to a large saucepan with enough water to come about 1¼ in (3 cm) above the beans. Bring to a simmer and cook for 1 hour. Drain well before adding to the soup. Boiled dried beans have a slightly lower GI value than canned beans. They also have a denser texture, making them slightly more filling.

nutrition per serving (6) Energy 220 Cal (923 kJ); Fat 5.3 g; Saturated fat 1.5 g; Protein 11.7 g; Carbohydrate 38.7 g; Fiber 5.1 g; Cholesterol 70 mg

minestrone primavera

This soup celebrates the return of warm weather with a mix of fresh green vegetables. It is a good source of folate and beta-carotene.

1 tbs canola or olive oil

2¼ oz (60 g) low-fat bacon (we used 97% fat-free), finely chopped

2 onions, chopped

2 garlic cloves, thinly sliced

2 small celery stalks, sliced

8 cups (70 fl oz/2 liters) chicken stock

⅓ cup (1¾ oz/50 g) macaroni

2 zucchini (courgettes), chopped

2 cups (5½ oz/150 g) shredded savoy cabbage

6 oz (175 g) green beans, trimmed and chopped

1 cup (5½ oz/150 g) frozen peas

1 cup (1½ oz/40 g) shredded spinach leaves

14 oz (400 g) can cannellini beans, drained and rinsed

1 large handful basil, chopped

grated Parmesan cheese, to serve

Prep time: 25 minutes

Cooking time: 40 minutes

Serves 4–6

Heat the oil in a large saucepan. Add the bacon, onion, garlic and celery and cook over low heat for 8 minutes, stirring occasionally until the vegetables are soft but not brown. Add the stock and bring to a boil. Simmer, covered, for 10 minutes.

Add the macaroni and boil for 12 minutes, or until almost *al dente*. Stir in the zucchini, cabbage, beans and peas and simmer for 5 minutes. Add the spinach, cannellini beans and basil and simmer for 2 minutes. Season to taste and serve with the grated Parmesan.

nutrition per serving (6) Energy 181 Cal (759 kJ); Fat 5.3 g; Saturated fat 1.2 g; Protein 13.8 g; Carbohydrate 20.6 g; Fiber 7.8 g; Cholesterol 20 mg

mediterranean fish soup

This delicious soup evokes the warmth of the Mediterranean and is a great way to include fish in your diet. It delivers significant amounts of protein, antioxidants, B-group vitamins and minerals.

½ tsp saffron threads

2 tsp olive oil

2 large onions, thinly sliced

1 leek, chopped

4 garlic cloves, finely chopped

1 bay leaf, torn

½ tsp dried marjoram

1 tsp grated orange zest

2 tbs dry white wine

1 red pepper (capsicum), cut into bite-size pieces

1 lb 2 oz (500 g) ripe tomatoes, chopped

½ cup (4 fl oz/125 ml) tomato purée

2 cups (17 fl oz/500 ml) fish stock

2 tbs tomato paste

2 tsp soft brown sugar

1 lb 2 oz (500 g) skinless and boneless fish fillets, trimmed and cut into bite-size pieces (see Hints)

3 tbs chopped parsley

4 wholegrain bread rolls or slices

Soak the saffron threads in a small bowl with 2 tablespoons of boiling water.

Heat the oil in a large saucepan over low heat. Add the onion, leek, garlic, bay leaf and marjoram. Cover and cook for 10 minutes, shaking the pan occasionally until the onion is soft. Add the zest, wine, pepper and tomato, cover and cook for 10 minutes.

Add the tomato purée, fish stock, tomato paste, sugar and saffron (with the liquid) to the pan. Stir well and bring to a boil, then reduce the heat to low and simmer, uncovered, for 15 minutes.

Add the fish to the soup, cover and cook for 8 minutes, or until tender. Add half the parsley, then season to taste with salt and freshly ground black pepper. Discard the bay leaf. Sprinkle the soup with the remaining parsley just before serving.

Warm the bread, then serve with the soup.

HINTS: Try catfish, red mullet, cod or ocean perch.

Prep time: 30 minutes

Cooking time: 45 minutes

Serves 4

nutrition per serving Energy 381 Cal (1601 kJ);
Fat 7.1 g; Saturated fat 1.5 g; Protein 36.3 g;
Carbohydrate 40.6 g; Fiber 8.6 g; Cholesterol 77 mg

pea and ham soup

A family favorite—this delicious soup is nourishing and satisfying and is a great way to include more legumes in your diet.

2 cups (1 lb/450 g) green split peas

1 lb 10 oz (750 g) ham bones

1 celery stalk, including leaves, chopped

1 carrot, chopped

1 onion, chopped

3 leeks, sliced

1 sweet potato, peeled and chopped

Prep time: 20 minutes + soaking time

Cooking time: 2½ hours

Serves 4–6

Put the split peas in a large bowl, cover with water and leave to soak for at least 4 hours or overnight. Drain and rinse well.

Put the ham bones, split peas, celery, carrot and onion in a large saucepan with 10 cups (87 fl oz/2.5 liters) water. Bring to a boil, then reduce the heat and simmer, covered, for 2 hours, or until the split peas are very soft.

Add the leek and sweet potato to the pan and cook for 30 minutes, or until the vegetables are tender and the ham is falling off the bone. Remove the ham bones from the soup; cut off all the meat and finely chop.

Transfer the soup to a bowl to cool, then use a potato masher to lightly mash—the soup should be chunky. Return the soup to the pan, stir in the chopped ham and reheat the soup to serve. Either serve on its own as a starter or serve with oven-toasted wholegrain bread and a mixed salad for a complete meal.

HINT: Some ham can be quite salty—soaking the bone in cold water overnight will draw out a lot of the saltiness. Always taste at the end of cooking before adding extra salt.

nutrition per serving (6) Energy 296 Cal (1240 kJ); Fat 3.6 g; Saturated fat 0.8 g; Protein 24.9 g; Carbohydrate 4.6 g; Fiber 9.8 g; Cholesterol 17 mg

lentil, bulghur wheat and mint soup

You can taste the goodness in this colorful, sustaining soup. It will keep in the refrigerator for up to 4 days—bring to a boil before serving.

2 tomatoes

2 tsp olive oil

I large red onion, finely chopped

2 garlic cloves, crushed

2 tbs tomato paste

2 tsp ground paprika

½ tsp cayenne pepper

2 cups (14 oz/400 g) red lentils

¼ cup (1¾ oz/50 g) basmati rice

8½ cups (74 fl oz/2.125 liters) chicken stock

¼ cup (1¾ oz/50 g) fine bulghur wheat (burghul)

2 tbs chopped mint

2 tbs chopped Italian (flat-leaf) parsley

⅓ cup (3 oz/85 g) low-fat plain yogurt

¼ preserved lemon, pulp removed, zest washed and julienned

Prep time: 25 minutes

Cooking time: 45 minutes

Serves 4–6

To peel the tomatoes, score a cross in the base of each one. Cover with boiling water for 30 seconds, then plunge into cold water. Drain and peel away the tomato skin from the cross. Finely chop the flesh.

Heat the oil in a large saucepan over medium heat. Add the onion and garlic and cook for 2–3 minutes, or until soft. Stir in the tomato paste, fresh tomato and spices and cook for I minute.

Add the lentils, rice and stock, then cover and bring to a boil over high heat. Reduce the heat and simmer for 30–35 minutes, or until the rice is cooked.

Stir in the bulghur wheat and herbs, then season to taste with salt and freshly ground black pepper. Divide the soup among bowls, garnish with yogurt and preserved lemon and serve immediately.

HINTS: This soup will thicken on standing, so if reheating you may need to add more liquid.

To make this a vegetarian soup, simply replace the chicken stock with vegetable stock.

nutrition per serving (6) Energy 286 Cal (1198 kJ); Fat 4.8 g; Saturated fat 1.2 g; Protein 23 g; Carbohydrate 39.3 g; Fiber 11.3 g; Cholesterol 1 mg

thai-style chicken and corn soup

This is a great recipe for busy people—it can be prepared in less than 30 minutes if you have all the ingredients on hand.

15 oz (425 g) can corn kernels, undrained

2 chicken bouillon (stock) cubes, crumbled

8 scallions (spring onions), sliced

1 tbs finely chopped fresh ginger

1 lb 2 oz (500 g) boneless skinless chicken breast, trimmed and thinly sliced

1 tbs sweet chili sauce

1 tbs fish sauce

7 oz (200 g) fresh thin rice noodles

2 large handfuls cilantro (coriander) leaves, chopped

2 tsp grated lime zest

2 tbs lime juice

Prep time: 15 minutes
Cooking time: 10 minutes
Serves 4

Bring 4 cups (35 fl oz/1 liter) water to a boil in a large saucepan over high heat. Add the corn kernels and their juice, the bouillon cubes, scallion and ginger, then reduce the heat and simmer for 1 minute.

Add the chicken, sweet chili sauce and fish sauce and simmer for 3 minutes, or until the chicken is cooked through.

Put the noodles in a large heatproof bowl, cover with boiling water and soak for 5 minutes, or until softened. Separate gently and drain.

Add the noodles, cilantro, lime zest and lime juice to the soup and serve immediately.

nutrition per serving Energy 363 Cal (1525 kJ); Fat 8.4 g; Saturated fat 2.3 g; Protein 32.4 g; Carbohydrate 39 g; Fiber 3.8 g; Cholesterol 83 mg

gazpacho

This delicious chilled soup originated in Spain and is really refreshing in warm summer weather. It can be served as a starter or a main meal.

1 lb 10 oz (750 g) ripe tomatoes

1 small (Lebanese) cucumber, chopped

1 green pepper (capsicum), chopped

2 garlic cloves, crushed

2 tbs finely chopped black olives

2–3 tbs red or white wine vinegar

1 tbs olive oil

1 tbs tomato paste

ACCOMPANIMENTS

2 eggs

1 onion, finely chopped

1 red pepper (capsicum), finely chopped

2 scallions (spring onions), finely chopped

1 short cucumber, finely chopped

chopped mint or parsley, to serve

Prep time: 40 minutes + 3 hours refrigeration

Cooking time: 5 minutes

Serves 4–6

To peel the tomatoes, score a cross in the base of each one. Cover with boiling water for 30 seconds, then plunge into cold water. Drain and peel away the tomato skin from the cross. Chop the flesh so finely that it is almost a purée.

Mix together the tomato, cucumber, pepper, garlic, olives, vinegar, oil and tomato paste, and season to taste with salt and freshly ground black pepper. Cover and refrigerate for 2–3 hours.

Meanwhile, fill a saucepan with cold water and gently add the eggs. Bring to a boil, then reduce the heat and simmer for 6 minutes. Drain and plunge the eggs into cold water to stop the cooking process. Peel and chop.

Use 2–3 cups (17–26 fl oz/500–750 ml) of chilled water to thin the soup to your taste. Serve chilled, with the chopped boiled egg, onion, pepper, scallion, cucumber and herbs served separately for diners to add to their own bowls.

HINTS: Keep refrigerated and consume within 2 days. It is unsuitable to freeze.

Serve with crusty wholegrain bread or pumpernickel for a satisfying main meal.

nutrition per serving (6) Energy 95 Cal (398 kJ); Fat 5.2 g; Saturated fat 1 g; Protein 4.6 g; Carbohydrate 7 g; Fiber 2.9 g; Cholesterol 72 mg

roasted red pepper soup

Roasted red peppers and tomatoes are a great flavor combination and make this vegetarian soup a rich source of the antioxidant, beta-carotene.

4 large red peppers (capsicums)

4 ripe tomatoes

2 tsp olive or canola oil

1 red onion, chopped

1 garlic clove, crushed

4 cups (35 fl oz/1 liter) vegetable stock

1 tsp sweet chili sauce

Parmesan cheese, to serve

pesto, to serve

6 thick slices wholegrain bread

Prep time: 30 minutes
Cooking time: 45 minutes
Serves 6

Cut the peppers into large flat pieces, removing the seeds and membrane. Put skin-side-up under a hot broiler (grill) until blackened. Leave covered with a dish towel until cool, then peel away the skin and chop the flesh.

To peel the tomatoes, score a cross in the base of each one. Cover with boiling water for 30 seconds, then plunge into cold water. Drain and peel away the tomato skin from the cross. Cut in half, scoop out the seeds and roughly chop the flesh.

Heat the oil in a large frying pan and add the onion. Cook over medium heat for 10 minutes, stirring frequently, until very soft. Add the garlic and cook for a further minute. Add the pepper, tomato and stock; bring to a boil, reduce the heat and simmer for about 20 minutes.

Coarsely purée the soup in a food processor or blender (in batches if necessary). Return to the pan to reheat gently and stir in the chili sauce. Top with shavings of Parmesan and a little pesto. Serve with sliced wholegrain bread.

HINT: The GI will vary depending on how finely puréed the soup is.

nutrition per serving Energy 174 Cal (730 kJ); Fat 3.8 g; Saturated fat 0.6 g; Protein 8.5 g; Carbohydrate 26.1 g; Fiber 4.6 g; Cholesterol 0 mg

country-style vegetable soup

A satisfying soup the whole family will enjoy, and an easy way to include a variety of different vegetables in your diet.

1 cup (8 oz/225 g) soup mix or pearl barley

2 tsp canola or olive oil

1 large onion, finely chopped

1 green pepper (capsicum), chopped

2 zucchini (courgettes), sliced

2 celery stalks, sliced

4½ oz (125 g) button mushrooms, sliced

2 carrots, sliced

1 sweet potato, peeled and chopped

13 oz (375 g) winter squash (pumpkin), peeled and chopped

8 cups (70 fl oz/2 liters) vegetable stock

Prep time: 25 minutes + overnight soaking

Cooking time: 55 minutes

Serves 6

Put the soup mix or barley in a large bowl, cover with water and leave to soak for 8 hours, or overnight. Drain and rinse well.

Heat the oil in a large saucepan and cook the onion for 5 minutes, or until soft. Add the pepper, zucchini, celery and mushrooms and cook for 5 minutes, or until starting to become soft. Add the carrot, sweet potato, pumpkin and soup mix and stir well.

Pour in the stock and bring to a boil. Reduce the heat to low, partially cover the pan with a lid and simmer for 45 minutes, or until the vegetables and soup mix are just soft. For a thinner soup add a little water.

HINTS: The soup will keep for 2 days in the refrigerator or in the freezer for 1 month. Bring to a boil before serving.

Soup mix is a combination of pearl barley, split peas and lentils. Both pearl barley and soup mix are readily available from supermarkets.

nutrition per serving Energy 220 Cal (923 kJ); Fat 4.2 g; Saturated fat 1.1 g; Protein 10.5 g; Carbohydrate 34.8 g; Fiber 7.4 g; Cholesterol 0 mg

tuna, white bean and tomato salad

Ready in under 30 minutes, this meal is a good choice for a quick and healthy weekday meal. Serve with wholegrain bread for a complete meal.

3 eggs

5 x 6 oz (175 g) cans tuna in brine or spring water

1 garlic clove, crushed

1 tbs roughly chopped thyme

1 tbs finely chopped parsley

½ cup (4 fl oz/125 ml) fat-free Italian dressing

14 oz (400 g) can cannellini beans, drained and rinsed

1 large red onion, coarsely chopped

3 ripe tomatoes, cut into wedges

Prep time: 20 minutes
Cooking time: 5 minutes
Serves 4–6

Fill a saucepan with cold water and gently add the eggs. Bring to a boil, then reduce the heat and simmer for 6 minutes. Drain and plunge the eggs into cold water to stop the cooking process. Peel and cut into wedges.

Drain the tuna and flake into chunks. Combine the garlic, thyme, parsley and dressing in a bowl, and whisk with a fork. Season to taste with salt and freshly ground black pepper.

Combine the beans and onion in a large bowl, add the dressing and toss. Add the tuna, toss gently, then add half the egg wedges and half the tomato. Lightly combine. Pile on a platter and garnish with the remaining egg and tomato.

nutrition per serving (6) Energy 235 Cal (988 kJ); Fat 5.4 g; Saturated fat 1.8 g; Protein 32.5 g; Carbohydrate 14 g; Fiber 4.7 g; Cholesterol 146 mg

salad niçoise

This Mediterranean salad is rich in flavor and provides a good range of vitamins and minerals. Use eggs enriched with omega-3 essential fat to boost your intake of this healthy fat.

4 eggs

9 oz (250 g) green beans, trimmed

6 artichoke hearts in brine, drained

12 oz (350 g) mixed salad leaves

4 tomatoes, cut into wedges

15 oz (425 g) can tuna in brine or spring water, drained and separated into chunks

1 red pepper (capsicum), cut into strips

14 oz (400 g) can cannellini beans, drained and rinsed

1 tbs capers

10 small black olives

1 tbs chopped tarragon

DRESSING

1 garlic clove, crushed

3 tsp Dijon mustard

2 anchovy fillets in brine, drained and finely chopped

½ cup (4 fl oz/125 ml) fat-free French dressing

Prep time: 25 minutes

Cooking time: 10 minutes

Serves 4–6

Fill a saucepan with cold water and gently add the eggs. Bring to a boil, then reduce the heat and simmer for 6 minutes. Drain and plunge the eggs into cold water to stop the cooking process. Peel and cut into wedges.

Put the beans in a saucepan of boiling water, return to a boil for 2 minutes, then drain and rinse under cold water. Chill in a bowl of ice water. Cut the artichokes into halves or quarters.

Arrange the salad leaves on a platter or individual plates. Top with the ,tomato, artichoke, tuna, egg, red pepper, green bean and cannellini beans. Sprinkle with the capers and olives.

To make the dressing, put the garlic, mustard, anchovies and dressing in a bowl and whisk until well blended. Season with salt and freshly ground black pepper and drizzle over the salad. Sprinkle with tarragon.

nutrition per serving (6) Energy 217 Cal (912 kJ); Fat 5.6 g; Saturated fat 1.6 g; Protein 24.6 g; Carbohydrate 17.1 g; Fiber 8.4 g; Cholesterol 152 mg

warm shrimp, arugula and feta salad

This colorful salad will impress your friends and family, and is suitable as a starter or a main meal. It provides antioxidants and minerals.

2 lb 4 oz (1 kg) raw shrimp (prawns)

4 scallions (spring onions), chopped

4 plum (Roma) tomatoes, chopped

1 red pepper (capsicum), chopped

14 oz (400 g) can chickpeas, drained and rinsed

1 tbs chopped dill

3 tbs finely shredded basil

1 tbs extra virgin olive oil

¾ oz (20 g) canola or olive oil margarine

2 small fresh red chilies, finely chopped

4 garlic cloves, crushed

2 tbs lemon juice

10½ oz (300 g) arugula (rocket)

4½ oz (125 g) low-fat feta cheese

Prep time: 30 minutes
Cooking time: 10 minutes
Serves 4–6

Peel the shrimp, leaving the tails intact. Gently pull out the dark vein from each shrimp back, starting at the head end.

Combine the scallion, tomato, pepper, chickpeas and herbs in a bowl.

Heat the oil and margarine in a large frying pan or wok, add the shrimp and cook, stirring over high heat for 3 minutes. Add the chili and garlic, and continue cooking until the shrimp turn pink. Remove from the heat and stir in the lemon juice.

Arrange the arugula leaves on a large platter, top with the tomato mixture, then the shrimp mixture. Crumble the feta cheese over the top.

nutrition per serving (6) Energy 240 Cal (1004 kJ); Fat 10.3 g; Saturated fat 3 g; Protein 27.5 g; Carbohydrate 9.3 g; Fiber 4.1 g; Cholesterol 137 mg

three-bean salad

This colorful salad is a great dish to serve at barbecues and picnics and is ready in a flash. Canned legumes are a great time-saver and have the added benefit of being highly nutritious and low GI.

9 oz (250 g) green beans, trimmed

14 oz (400 g) can chickpeas, drained and rinsed

14 oz (400 g) can red kidney beans, drained and rinsed

14 oz (400 g) can cannellini beans, drained and rinsed

11 oz (310 g) can corn kernels, drained and rinsed

3 scallions (spring onions), sliced

1 red pepper (capsicum), chopped

3 celery stalks, chopped

4–6 dill pickles (gherkins), chopped

3 tbs chopped mint

3 tbs chopped Italian (flat-leaf) parsley

MUSTARD VINAIGRETTE

½ cup (4 fl oz/125 ml) fat-free French dressing

1 tbs Dijon mustard

1 garlic clove, crushed

Prep time: 25 minutes
Cooking time: 5 minutes
Serves 8–10

Cut the green beans into short lengths. Bring a small saucepan of water to a boil, add the beans and cook for 2 minutes. Drain and rinse under cold water, then leave in ice water until cold. Drain.

Put the green beans, chickpeas, kidney beans, cannellini beans, corn, scallion, pepper, celery, dill pickle, mint and parsley in a large bowl. Season with salt and freshly ground black pepper and mix together.

To make the vinaigrette, put the dressing, mustard and garlic in a small bowl and whisk until well blended. Drizzle the vinaigrette over the salad and toss gently.

HINTS: The salad can be prepared up to 3 hours in advance and refrigerated, but don't add the dressing until just before serving.

You can make this dish using dried beans and peas. Remember to soak the beans in cold water overnight, then drain and cook in boiling water until tender. Check the package for cooking times as some beans take longer than others and may need to be cooked separately.

nutrition per serving (10) Energy 132 Cal (554 kJ); Fat 1.1 g; Saturated fat 0.1 g; Protein 6.8 g; Carbohydrate 20.4 g; Fiber 6.7 g; Cholesterol 0 mg

asparagus and mushroom salad

This stylish salad is ideal as a starter or as a side dish with meat or fish. The flavors and textures of the mushrooms and asparagus complement each other perfectly.

1 bunch (6 oz/175 g) asparagus, trimmed

1 tbs grain mustard

1 tbs grated orange zest

2 tsp grated lemon zest

2 tsp grated lime zest

3 tbs orange juice

2 tbs lemon juice

1 tbs lime juice

2 garlic cloves, crushed

2 tsp sugar

14 oz (400 g) button mushrooms, halved

5½ oz (150 g) arugula (rocket)

1 red pepper (capsicum), cut into strips

Prep time: 20 minutes
Cooking time: 10 minutes
Serves 4

Snap the woody ends from the asparagus spears and cut in half on the diagonal. Cook in boiling water for 1 minute, or until just tender. Drain, plunge into cold water and set aside.

Put the mustard, citrus zest and juice, garlic and sugar in a large saucepan and season with freshly ground black pepper. Bring to a boil, then reduce the heat and add the mushrooms, tossing for 2 minutes. Cool.

Remove the mushrooms from the sauce with a slotted spoon. Return the sauce to the heat, bring to a boil, then reduce the heat and simmer for 3–5 minutes, or until reduced. Cool slightly.

Toss the mushrooms, arugula leaves, pepper and asparagus together. Put on a plate and drizzle with the sauce.

nutrition per serving Energy 68 Cal (287 kJ); Fat 0.8 g; Saturated fat 0.01 g; Protein 6.6 g; Carbohydrate 8.2 g; Fiber 4.6 g; Cholesterol 0 mg

chickpea and roast vegetable salad

This is a nutritious and satisfying vegetarian meal or side dish. It is low in fat and rich in beta-carotene.

1 lb 2 oz (500 g) orange sweet potato, peeled and cubed

2 red peppers (capsicums), halved

4 slender eggplants (aubergines), halved lengthwise

4 zucchini (courgettes), halved lengthwise

4 onions, quartered

canola or olive oil spray

2 x 10½ oz (300 g) cans chickpeas, drained and rinsed

2 tbs chopped Italian (flat-leaf) parsley

DRESSING

½ cup (4 fl oz/125 ml) fat-free Italian dressing

1 garlic clove, crushed

1 tbs chopped thyme

Prep time: 25 minutes + 30 minutes standing
Cooking time: 40 minutes
Serves 8

Preheat the oven to 425°F (220°C/Gas 7). Line two baking sheets with baking paper and lay out the vegetables in a single layer. Lightly spray with oil.

Bake for 40 minutes, or until the vegetables are tender and begin to brown slightly on the edges. Cool. Remove the skins from the peppers if desired. Chop the pepper, eggplant and zucchini into pieces, then put the vegetables in a bowl with the chickpeas and half the parsley.

Whisk together the dressing ingredients. Season with salt and freshly ground black pepper, then toss with the vegetables. Leave for 30 minutes, then sprinkle with the rest of the parsley before serving.

nutrition per serving Energy 137 Cal (577 kJ); Fat 1.9 g; Saturated fat 0.2 g; Protein 6.2 g; Carbohydrate 23.8 g; Fiber 5.8 g; Cholesterol 0 mg

tofu salad with ginger miso dressing

This Asian-themed salad is a delicious light vegetarian meal or side dish. Serve with fresh rice noodles or basmati rice.

4½ tbs tamari

1 tsp soy bean oil

2 garlic cloves, crushed

1 tsp grated fresh ginger

1 tsp chili paste

1 lb 2 oz (500 g) firm tofu, cut into small cubes

14 oz (400 g) mixed Asian salad leaves

1 short (Lebanese) cucumber, thinly sliced

9 oz (250 g) cherry tomatoes, halved

canola or olive oil spray

DRESSING

2 tsp white miso paste

2 tbs mirin

1 tsp sesame oil

1 tsp grated fresh ginger

1 tsp finely chopped chives

1 tbs sesame seeds, toasted

Prep time: 20 minutes + 10 minutes marinating

Cooking time: 5 minutes

Serves 4

Mix together the tamari, soy bean oil, garlic, ginger, chili paste and ½ teaspoon salt in a bowl. Add the tofu and mix until well coated. Marinate for at least 10 minutes. Drain, reserving the marinade.

Put the salad leaves, cucumber and tomato in a bowl.

To make the dressing, combine the miso with ½ cup (4 fl oz/125 ml) hot water and leave until the miso dissolves. Add the mirin, sesame oil, ginger, chives and sesame seeds and stir until it begins to thicken.

Heat a charbroil pan or barbecue hotplate to hot. Spray with oil. Add the tofu and cook over medium heat for 4 minutes, or until golden brown. Increase the heat to high, pour on the reserved marinade and cook for a further 1 minute over high heat. Remove from the charbroil pan and cool for 5 minutes.

Add the tofu to the salad, drizzle with the dressing and toss well.

HINTS: Tamari is a naturally fermented, thick, dark Japanese soy sauce. You can use normal soy sauce instead.

Miso is Japanese bean paste and is commonly used in soups, dressings, on broiled foods and as a flavoring for pickles.

Mirin is a rice liquid sometimes referred to as sweet rice wine.

nutrition per serving Energy 224 Cal (942 kJ); Fat 13.5 g; Saturated fat 1.9 g; Protein 18.8 g; Carbohydrate 6.6 g; Fiber 5.6 g; Cholesterol 0 mg

warm marinated mushroom salad

The zesty marinade perfectly complements and highlights the flavours of the different mushrooms in this warm salad.

1 lb 10 oz (750 g) mixed mushrooms

2 garlic cloves, finely chopped

½ teaspoon green peppercorns, crushed

2 tbs olive oil

4 tbs freshly squeezed orange juice

9 oz (250 g) salad leaves (such as watercress or baby English spinach leaves)

canola or olive oil spray

1 tsp finely grated orange zest

Prep time: 25 minutes + 20 minutes marinating

Cooking time: 5 minutes

Serves 4

Trim the mushroom stems and wipe the mushrooms with a damp paper towel. Cut any large mushrooms in half. Mix together the garlic, peppercorns, olive oil and orange juice. Pour over the mushrooms and marinate for about 20 minutes.

Arrange the salad leaves in a dish.

Heat a charbroil pan or barbecue hotplate to hot. Spray with oil. Drain the mushrooms, reserving the marinade. First cook the flat and button mushrooms on the charbroil pan for about 2 minutes. Add the softer mushrooms and cook for 1 minute, or until they just soften.

Sprinkle the mushrooms over the salad leaves and drizzle with the marinade. Sprinkle with orange zest and season well with salt and freshly ground black pepper.

HINT: Try a mix of mushrooms, such as baby button, oyster, straw, shiitake and enoki.

nutrition per serving Energy 138 Cal (580 kJ); Fat 9.8 g; Saturated fat 1.3 g; Protein 7.9 g; Carbohydrate 4.8 g; Fiber 8.5 g; Cholesterol 0 mg

pesto beef salad

This zesty pasta salad is a great choice for people who need to eat more iron. It also provides good amounts of the antioxidants, vitamin C and beta-carotene. It is suitable as a main meal.

1 large red pepper (capsicum)

1 large yellow pepper (capsicum)

canola or olive oil spray

3½ oz (100 g) lean beef tenderloin (fillet) steak, trimmed

4½ oz (125 g) penne

3½ oz (100 g) button mushrooms, quartered

PESTO

½ bunch basil (about 1¾ oz/ 50 g leaves)

2 garlic cloves, chopped

2 tbs pumpkin seeds (pepitas)

1 tbs olive oil

2 tbs orange juice

1 tbs lemon juice

Prep time: 30 minutes
Cooking time: 25 minutes
Serves 4

Cut the peppers into large flat pieces, removing the seeds and membrane. Put skin-side-up under a hot broiler (grill) until blackened. Leave covered with a dish towel until cool, then peel away the skin and chop the flesh.

Spray a non-stick frying pan with oil and cook the steak over high heat for 3–4 minutes on each side. Remove and leave for 5 minutes before cutting into thin slices. Season with a little salt.

To make the pesto, finely chop the basil, garlic and pumpkin seeds in a food processor. With the motor running, add the oil, orange and lemon juice. Season well with salt and freshly ground black pepper.

Meanwhile, cook the pasta in a large saucepan of boiling water for 10 minutes, or until *al dente*. Drain well and toss with the pesto in a large bowl.

Add the pepper pieces, steak slices and mushroom quarters to the penne and toss to distribute evenly. Serve immediately.

nutrition per serving Energy 239 Cal (1005 kJ); Fat 9.5 g; Saturated fat 1.7 g; Protein 12.4 g; Carbohydrate 25.8 g; Fiber 3.7 g; Cholesterol 17 mg

tabbouleh

This popular salad is very versatile—serve it with meat or fish, use it in a sandwich or eat it on its own. If you like to experiment, look for cracked barley in health food shops to use as a substitute for the bulghur wheat.

¾ cup (4½ oz/125 g) bulghur wheat (burghul)

2 large bunches (about 10½ oz/300 g) Italian (flat-leaf) parsley

1 handful mint leaves

4 scallions (spring onions), finely chopped

4 tomatoes, finely chopped

2 garlic cloves, crushed

3 tbs lemon juice

2 tbs olive oil

Prep time: 20 minutes + 15 minutes standing

Cooking time: 0

Serves 6–8

Put the bulghur wheat in a bowl with 3¾ cups (6 fl oz/185 ml) water and leave for 15 minutes, or until all the water has been absorbed.

Finely chop the herbs with a large sharp knife or in a food processor. Take care not to over-process.

Put the bulghur wheat, herbs, scallion, tomato, garlic, lemon juice and oil in a bowl and toss well. Refrigerate until required. Return to room temperature to serve.

nutrition per serving (8) Energy 109 Cal (460 kJ); Fat 5 g; Saturated fat 0.7 g; Protein 3.8 g; Carbohydrate 11.5 g; Fiber 6.1 g; Cholesterol 0 mg

spicy lentil salad

Serve on its own or as a side with broiled fish, poultry or meat.

1 cup (8 oz/225 g) basmati rice

1 cup (6 oz/175 g) brown lentils

1 tsp turmeric

1 tsp ground cinnamon

6 cardamom pods

3 star anise

2 bay leaves

3 tbs canola oil

1 tbs lemon juice

9 oz (250 g) broccoli florets

2 carrots, cut into julienne strips

1 onion, finely chopped

2 garlic cloves, crushed

1 red pepper (capsicum), finely chopped

1 tsp garam masala

1 tsp ground coriander

1⅔ cups (9 oz/250 g) fresh or frozen peas, thawed

DRESSING

1 cup (9 oz/250 g) plain yogurt

1 tbs lemon juice

1 tbs chopped mint

1 tsp cumin seeds

Prep time: 30 minutes

Cooking time: 1¼ hours

Serves 6

Put the rice, lentils, turmeric, cinnamon, cardamom, star anise and bay leaves in a saucepan with 3 cups (26 fl oz/750 ml) water. Stir well and bring to a boil. Reduce the heat, cover and simmer gently for 50–60 minutes, or until the liquid is absorbed. Remove the whole spices. Transfer the mixture to a large bowl. Whisk 2 tablespoons of the oil with the lemon juice, then fork through the rice mixture.

Steam or boil the broccoli and carrots until tender. Drain and refresh in cold water.

Heat the remaining oil in a large frying pan and add the onion, garlic and pepper. Stir-fry for 2–3 minutes, then add the garam masala and coriander and stir-fry for a further 1–2 minutes. Add the cooked vegetables and peas and toss to coat in the spice mixture. Add to the rice and fork through to combine. Cover and refrigerate until cold.

To make the dressing, mix the yogurt, lemon juice, mint and cumin seeds together, and season with salt and freshly ground black pepper. Spoon the salad into six individual bowls or onto a platter and serve with the dressing.

nutrition per serve Energy 381 Cal (1601 kJ); Fat 12 g; Saturated fat 1.4 g; Protein 17.4 g; Carbohydrate 51.5 g; Fiber 11.2 g; Cholesterol 4 mg

warm lamb salad

This salad is a good source of iron, zinc and antioxidants.

2 tbs red curry paste

3 tbs chopped cilantro (coriander) leaves

1 tbs finely grated fresh ginger

1 tbs peanut oil

1 lb 10 oz (750 g) lamb tenderloin (fillet), trimmed and thinly sliced

7 oz (200 g) snow peas (mangetout), trimmed

1 lb 5 oz (600 g) fresh rice noodles

canola or olive oil spray

1 red pepper (capsicum), thinly sliced

1 cucumber, thinly sliced

6 scallions (spring onions), thinly sliced

DRESSING

1 tbs peanut oil

3 tbs lime juice

2 tsp soft brown sugar

3 tsp fish sauce

3 tsp soy sauce

4 tbs chopped mint leaves

1 garlic clove, crushed

Prep time: 30 minutes + 3 hours refrigeration

Cooking time: 15 minutes

Serves 4–6

Combine the curry paste, cilantro, ginger and oil in a bowl. Add the lamb and coat well. Cover and refrigerate for 2–3 hours.

Steam or boil the snow peas until just tender, then refresh under cold water and drain.

Put the noodles in a large heatproof bowl, cover with boiling water and soak for 8 minutes, or until softened. Separate gently and drain.

To make the dressing, put all the ingredients in a small bowl and whisk until well blended.

Heat a wok until very hot. Spray with the oil. Add half the lamb and stir-fry for 5 minutes, or until tender. Repeat with the remaining lamb, using more spray oil if needed.

Put the lamb, snow peas, noodles, pepper, cucumber and scallion in a large bowl, drizzle with the dressing and toss together before serving.

nutrition per serving (6) Energy 445 Cal (1870 kJ); Fat 14.3 g; Saturated fat 3.4 g; Protein 32.1 g; Carbohydrate 46.6 g; Fiber 3.7 g; Cholesterol 81 mg

spicy thai pork salad

This spicy salad gets top marks for good taste and has the added benefits of being heart healthy and quick to make. Serve with fresh rice noodles or mung bean noodles for a complete low-GI meal.

⅓ cup (1¾ oz/50 g) raw unsalted peanuts

2 tsp canola oil

2 stems lemon grass, white part only, thinly sliced

2 green chilies, finely chopped

1 lb 2 oz (500 g) lean ground (minced) pork

2 tsp finely grated lime zest

3 tbs lime juice

2–6 tsp chili sauce

lettuce leaves, to serve

1 handful cilantro (coriander) leaves

1 small handful small mint leaves

1 small onion, very finely sliced

3 tbs crisp-fried garlic

Prep time: 20 minutes

Cooking time: 10 minutes

Serves 4–6

Preheat the oven to 350°F (180°C/Gas 4). Put the peanuts on a baking sheet. Cook for 5 minutes, stirring once, until the peanuts are lightly golden. Cool then chop.

Heat a wok until very hot, add the oil and swirl to coat. Add the lemon grass, chili and pork. Stir-fry, breaking up any lumps with a fork or wooden spoon, over high heat for 6 minutes, or until cooked through. Transfer to a bowl and set aside to cool completely.

Add the lime zest, lime juice and the chili sauce to taste, to the cooled pork mixture. Arrange the lettuce leaves on a plate. Stir most of the cilantro and mint leaves, onion, peanuts and fried garlic through the pork mixture. Spoon over the lettuce and sprinkle the rest of the mint leaves, onion, peanuts and garlic over the top to serve.

HINT: Crisp-fried garlic is commonly available from Asian markets and also some supermarkets.

nutrition per serving (6) Energy 190 Cal (794 kJ); Fat 11.2 g; Saturated fat 2.8 g; Protein 19.1 g; Carbohydrate 2.9 g; Fiber 1.5 g; Cholesterol 50 mg

grilled tuna and white bean salad

This salad contains the satisfying combination of fish protein, fiber and low-GI carbohydrate from the beans—great if you're watching your weight.

14 oz (400 g) tuna steaks

cracked black pepper

1 small red onion, thinly sliced

1 tomato, seeded and chopped

1 small red pepper (capsicum), thinly sliced

2 x 14 oz (400 g) cans cannellini beans

2 garlic cloves, crushed

1 tsp chopped thyme

4 tbs finely chopped Italian (flat-leaf) parsley

4 tbs fat-free French dressing

3½ oz (100 g) arugula (rocket)

Prep time: 25 minutes
Cooking time: 5 minutes
Serves 4–6

Put the tuna steaks on a plate, sprinkle with cracked black pepper on both sides, cover with plastic and refrigerate until needed.

Combine the onion, tomato and pepper in a large bowl. Rinse the cannellini beans under cold running water for 30 seconds, drain and add to the bowl with the garlic, thyme and 3 tablespoons of the parsley.

Cook the tuna on a hot, lightly oiled barbecue grill or hot plate for 1 minute on each side. The meat should still be pink in the middle. Cut into small cubes and combine with the salad. Toss with the dressing.

Arrange the arugula on a platter. Top with the salad, season with salt and freshly ground black pepper and sprinkle with the remaining parsley.

nutrition per serving (6) Energy 202 Cal (848 kJ); Fat 4.4 g; Saturated fat 1.6 g; Protein 24.9 g; Carbohydrate 16.6 g; Fiber 7.1 g; Cholesterol 24 mg

thai beef salad

No wonder this salad is on the menu at so many cafés and restaurants—it combines the hearty goodness of beef with the exotic appeal of Asian flavors. Serve with basmati rice or fresh rice noodles for a low-GI meal.

3 garlic cloves, finely chopped

4 cilantro (coriander) roots, finely chopped

1 tbs canola oil

canola or olive oil spray

14 oz (400 g) piece lean rump or sirloin steak, trimmed

1 small soft-leaved lettuce

7 oz (200 g) cherry tomatoes, halved

1 short (Lebanese) cucumber, cut into chunks

4 scallions (spring onions), chopped

2 handfuls cilantro (coriander) leaves

DRESSING

2 tbs fish sauce

2 tbs lime juice

1 tbs soy sauce

2 tsp chopped fresh red chili

2 tsp soft brown sugar

Prep time: 35 minutes

Cooking time: 10 minutes

Serves 4

Combine the garlic, cilantro roots, oil and ½ teaspoon freshly ground black pepper. If you have a mortar and pestle, use it to finely grind the mixture. Alternatively, blend the mixture well in a food processor or spice blender. Spread evenly over the steak.

Heat a heavy-based frying pan or wok over high heat and spray with the oil. Add the steak to the pan and cook for about 4 minutes on each side, turning once only during the cooking time. Remove the steak from the pan and set aside to cool completely.

To make the dressing, combine the fish sauce, lime juice, soy sauce, chili and brown sugar in a small bowl, stirring until the sugar has dissolved.

Slice the cooled steak into thin strips across the grain. Arrange the lettuce on a plate and arrange the tomatoes on top, with the cucumber, scallion and strips of steak. Drizzle with the dressing and scatter the cilantro leaves over the top. Serve immediately.

HINT: Ground herbs and spices are used extensively for flavoring in Asian cooking. Small amounts can be ground with a mortar and pestle or a clean coffee grinder. For larger quantities, use a blender or food processor. To help clean the bowl after grinding spices, run some stale bread or rice through the processor.

nutrition per serving Energy 211 Cal (885 kJ); Fat 10.2 g; Saturated fat 2.4 g; Protein 24.2 g; Carbohydrate 5.6 g; Fiber 3 g; Cholesterol 64 mg

Instead of chips, dips, crackers and nuts, serve one of these healthy low-fat dips or snacks for friends, or one of the healthy light meals as a starter or for a light meal on its own. You can enjoy them on their own or share with guests. The recipes provide you with options for low-GI snacks, side dishes, hors d'oeuvres and light meals. These recipes will be a revelation for anyone who thinks low-GI eating is plain and boring.

starters & light meals

eggplant sambal

This low-fat sambal can be served as a side dish with curry or eaten as a dip with a couple of pappadums or some wholegrain bread for a low-GI snack.

2 eggplants (aubergines), halved

canola or olive oil spray

½ tsp ground turmeric

3 tbs lime juice

2 red chilies, seeded and finely diced

I red onion, diced

⅓ cup (3¼ oz/90 g) thick plain yogurt

Prep time: 15 minutes
Cooking time: 30 minutes
Serves 4

Preheat the oven to 400°F (200°C/Gas 6). Put the eggplants in a roasting pan, cut side up. Spray the cut halves of the eggplants with the oil and sprinkle with the turmeric. Roast for 30 minutes, or until they are browned all over and very soft.

Scoop the eggplant pulp into a bowl, then mash with the lime juice, chili and red onion, reserving some chili and onion for garnish.

Season with salt, then fold in the yogurt. Garnish with the remaining onion and chili.

HINT: Pappadums are available at Indian markets.

nutrition per serving Energy 55 Cal (232 kJ); Fat 1.9 g; Saturated fat 0.6 g; Protein 3 g; Carbohydrate 5.9 g; Fiber 3.3 g; Cholesterol 4 mg

hummus

This popular dip is delicious on bread as a substitute for margarine or butter or great as a snack with some fresh carrot and celery stalks. It is also delicious with tabbouleh on pita bread.

1 cup (8 oz/225 g) dried chickpeas

2 tbs tahini

4 garlic cloves, crushed

4 tbs lemon juice, plus extra (optional)

2 tbs olive oil

2 tsp ground cumin

large pinch cayenne pepper

½ tsp salt

ground paprika, to garnish

1 tbs chopped parsley

Prep time: 20 minutes + overnight soaking

Cooking time: 1¼ hours

Serves 20

Put the chickpeas in a large bowl, cover with water and leave to soak overnight. Drain and rinse well.

Transfer the chickpeas to a large saucepan and cover with cold water. Bring to a boil, then reduce the heat and simmer for 1¼ hours, or until the chickpeas are very tender, occasionally skimming any froth from the surface. Drain well, reserving about 1 cup (9 fl oz/250 ml) of the cooking liquid and leave the chickpeas until cool enough to handle. Pick over for any loose skins and discard.

Process the chickpeas, tahini, garlic, lemon juice, olive oil, cumin, salt and cayenne pepper in a food processor until thick and smooth. With the motor still running, gradually add about ¾ cup (6 fl oz/185 ml) of the reserved cooking liquid to form a smooth creamy purée. Add extra lemon juice, to taste, if necessary.

Spread onto a flat bowl or plate, sprinkle with paprika and sprinkle the parsley over the top.

nutrition per serving Energy 58 Cal (245 kJ); Fat 3.7 g; Saturated fat 0.5 g; Protein 2.2 g; Carbohydrate 3.8 g; Fiber 1.7 g; Cholesterol 0 mg

white bean, chickpea and herb dip

This delicious dip contains less fat and calories than commercial cream-based dips and is great to snack on or serve at parties and barbecues with vegetable crudités. It is an easy way to eat more legumes and vegetables.

¾ cup (6 oz/175 g) dried cannellini beans

½ cup (3½ oz/100 g) dried chickpeas

3 slices wholegrain bread

3 tbs milk

2 scallions (spring onions), finely chopped

⅓ cup (3¼ oz/90 g) thick plain yogurt

1 tbs lemon juice

2 tsp finely grated lemon zest

1 tbs chopped parsley

2 tsp chopped oregano

1 tbs olive oil

Prep time: 20 minutes + overnight soaking

Cooking time: 1 hour

Serves 12

Put the cannellini beans and chickpeas in a large bowl, cover with water and leave to soak overnight. Drain and rinse well.

Transfer the beans and chickpeas to a large saucepan and cover with cold water. Bring to a boil, then reduce the heat and simmer for 1 hour, or until very tender, adding more water if needed. Skim any froth from the surface. Drain well, cool and mash.

Remove the crusts from the bread, put the bread in a bowl and drizzle with the milk. Leave for 2 minutes, then mash with your fingertips until very soft. Mix together with the beans.

Add the scallion, yogurt, lemon juice, zest, herbs and oil and season well with salt and freshly ground black pepper. Mix together well and serve at room temperature.

HINT: To make vegetable crudités, cut raw carrots, celery, zucchini (courgettes) and unpeeled short (Lebanese) cucumbers into 2¾ in (7 cm) sticks and raw cauliflower and broccoli into small florets.

nutrition per serving Energy 85 Cal (355 kJ); Fat 2.7 g; Saturated fat 0.6 g; Protein 4.8 g; Carbohydrate 10.3 g; Fiber 3.4 g; Cholesterol 2 mg

tzatziki

This low-calorie dip is delicious as a snack with crunchy raw vegetable crudités or as a low-fat substitute for mayonnaise in sandwiches and burgers.

2 short cucumbers
1⅔ cups (14 oz/400 g) low-fat plain yogurt
4 garlic cloves, crushed
3 tbs finely chopped mint, plus extra, to garnish
1 tbs lemon juice

Prep time: 10 minutes + 15 minutes standing
Cooking time: 0
Serves 12

Cut the cucumbers in half lengthwise, scoop out the seeds and discard. Leave the skin on and coarsely grate the cucumber into a small colander. Sprinkle with salt and leave over a large bowl for 15 minutes to drain off any bitter juices.

Meanwhile, stir together the yogurt, garlic, mint and lemon juice.

Rinse the cucumber under cold water then, taking small handfuls, squeeze out any excess moisture. Combine the grated cucumber with the yogurt mixture and season well with salt and freshly ground black pepper. Garnish with mint. Serve with crudités.

HINTS: Tzatziki will keep in an airtight container in the refrigerator for 2–3 days.

To make vegetable crudités, cut raw carrots, celery, zucchini (courgettes) and unpeeled short (Lebanese) cucumbers into 2¾ in (7 cm) sticks and raw cauliflower and broccoli into small florets.

nutrition per serving Energy 21 Cal (90 kJ);
Fat 0.1 g; Saturated fat 0.04 g; Protein 2.1 g;
Carbohydrate 2.5 g; Fiber 0.4 g; Cholesterol 2 mg

stuffed peppers

This colorful vegetarian dish will tempt your appetite and provide you with significant amounts of antioxidants and folate.

¾ cup (5½ oz/150 g) basmati rice, washed and drained

1⅓ cups (11 fl oz/325 ml) chicken stock

6 red, yellow or orange peppers (capsicums)

2 tsp olive oil

1 onion, finely chopped

½ celery stalk, finely chopped

1 small zucchini (courgette), finely chopped

½ cup (4½ oz/125 g) tomato purée

2 tbs chopped Italian (flat-leaf) parsley

2 tbs chopped mint

½ tsp ground cinnamon

⅓ cup (1¾ oz/50 g) pine nuts, lightly toasted

olive oil spray

Prep time: 30 minutes
Cooking time: 1 hour 10 minutes
Serves 6

Put the rice and stock in a saucepan and bring to a boil over medium heat. Reduce the heat, cover with a lid and cook for 20 minutes, or until the rice is tender. Remove from the heat and leave to stand, covered, for 5 minutes.

Bring a large saucepan of water to a boil. Cut the tops off the peppers, reserving them for use later. Remove and discard the seeds and membrane from inside the peppers. Blanch the peppers (not the lids) in the boiling water for 2 minutes. Drain and upturn on paper towels to dry.

Preheat the oven to 350°F (180°C/Gas 4). Heat the oil in a frying pan and cook the onion, celery and zucchini for 10 minutes, or until softened but not browned. Add the tomato purée, herbs, cinnamon, pine nuts and rice to the pan and stir for 2 minutes. Season with salt and freshly ground black pepper.

Sit the peppers in an ovenproof dish so they fit snugly. Divide the rice mixture among the pepper cavities. Replace the tops. Pour 3½ fl oz (100 ml) boiling water into the dish and lightly spray with oil over the tops of the peppers. Bake for 40 minutes, or until cooked through and tender.

nutrition per serving Energy 201 Cal (843 kJ); Fat 7.7 g; Saturated fat 0.6 g; Protein 5.8 g; Carbohydrate 26 g; Fiber 2.6 g; Cholesterol 1 mg

italian omelette

If you find plain omelettes a bit boring, this Italian-flavored version is the thing for you. The scent of fresh basil will invigorate you.

5½ oz (150 g) fusilli
(see Hint)

1 tsp olive oil

1 onion, finely chopped

4½ oz (125 g) low-fat ham,
sliced

6 eggs

3 tbs low-fat milk

¼ cup (1 oz/25 g) grated
Parmesan cheese

2 tbs chopped parsley

1 tbs chopped basil

canola or olive oil spray

½ cup (2¼ oz/60 g) grated
low-fat Cheddar cheese

wholegrain bread, to serve

Prep time: 20 minutes

Cooking time: 25 minutes

Serves 4

Cook the pasta in a large saucepan of boiling water for 10 minutes, or until *al dente*. Drain and cool.

Heat the oil in a non-stick frying pan. Add the onion and stir over low heat for 3–4 minutes, until tender. Add the ham and stir for 1 minute. Transfer to a plate.

Whisk together the eggs and milk and season well with salt and freshly ground black pepper. Stir in the pasta, Parmesan, herbs and onion mixture.

Preheat the broiler (grill). Heat the frying pan and spray with oil. Pour the egg mixture into the pan. Sprinkle with the Cheddar. Cook over medium heat until the omelette begins to set around the edges, then put the pan under the broiler until the omelette is set and lightly browned on top. Cut into wedges for serving. Serve with wholegrain bread.

HINT: You can use any short pasta.

Durum wheat pasta has a low-GI value. However, it should not be overcooked. Overcooking pasta until it is soft and soggy makes its starch more digestible and increases its GI value. Pasta should be served al dente.

nutrition per serving Energy 343 Cal (1442 kJ); Fat 13.4 g; Saturated fat 4,8 g; Protein 27.8 g; Carbohydrate 28 g; Fiber 1.7 g; Cholesterol 308 mg

chicken with peach, red pepper and bean salsa

An appetizing starter or light meal, this colorful dish is great if you love good food but don't have much time for cooking.

canola or olive oil spray

4 boneless, skinless chicken breasts

3 fresh peaches

5½ oz (150 g) baby green beans, trimmed

3 tbs white wine vinegar

1 tbs superfine (caster) sugar

2 tsp grated fresh ginger

1 garlic clove, crushed

½ tsp ground cumin

3 tbs chopped cilantro (coriander) leaves

3 tbs chopped mint

1 red pepper (capsicum), diced

1 small red onion, finely diced

1 small red chili, finely chopped

Prep time: 20 minutes
Cooking time: 15 minutes
Serves 4

Lightly spray a charbroil pan or indoor grill with oil and cook the chicken breasts for 5 minutes on each side, or until tender and cooked through.

Meanwhile, to peel the peaches, briefly plunge them into a bowl of boiling water. Refresh under cold water, then slip the skins from the peaches. Remove the stones, then dice the flesh.

Blanch the beans in a saucepan of boiling water for 2 minutes, then drain and refresh.

Combine the vinegar, sugar, ginger, garlic, cumin, cilantro and mint in a small bowl.

Put the pepper, onion, chili, peaches and beans in a large bowl. Gently stir through the vinegar herb mixture and serve immediately with the chicken.

nutrition per serving Energy 351 Cal (1468 kJ); Fat 11.7 g; Saturated fat 3.5 g; Protein 45.6 g; Carbohydrate 14.6 g; Fiber 3.4 g; Cholesterol 132 mg

baby octopus with ginger and lime

This flavorsome dish is rich in protein, vitamin A and iron, but low in fat. It's a great dish to add to your list of stir-fry favorites.

1 lb 2 oz (500 g) baby octopus

small handful chopped cilantro (coriander) leaves

2 garlic cloves, finely chopped

2 red chilies, seeded and chopped

2 tsp grated fresh ginger

2 stems lemon grass, white part only, chopped

2 tbs lime juice

1 tbs canola oil

14 oz (400 g) fresh thin rice noodles

canola or olive oil spray

12 oz (350 g) bok choy, leaves separated, washed, drained and chopped

14 oz (400 g) choy sum, leaves separated, washed, drained and chopped

1 tbs lime juice, extra

2 tbs oyster sauce

Prep time: 30 minutes + 2 hours marinating

Cooking time: 10 minutes

Serves 4

To prepare the baby octopus, remove the head, cut off the eyes, and remove the gut by slitting the head open. Grasp the body firmly and push the beak out with your index finger. Clean the octopus thoroughly under cold running water and pat dry with paper towels. Cut the head in half.

Put the octopus, cilantro, garlic, chili, ginger, lemon grass, lime juice and the oil in a non-metallic bowl. Cover and refrigerate overnight, or for at least 2 hours.

Put the noodles in a large heatproof bowl, cover with boiling water and soak for 8 minutes, or until softened. Separate gently and drain. Use scissors to cut into shorter lengths.

Heat a wok until very hot, spray with oil. Stir-fry the vegetables briefly, then add 1 tablespoon water, cover and steam for 1–2 minutes until just wilted. Toss through the noodles. Remove from the wok and keep warm.

Reheat the wok, spray with oil. Add the drained octopus and stir-fry over high heat for 2–3 minutes, or until cooked through. Combine the extra lime juice, oyster sauce and 2 tablespoons water. Just prior to serving toss through the noodles and wilted greens. Divide among 4 plates and serve.

nutrition per serving Energy 370 Cal (1547 kJ); Fat 6.1 g; Saturated fat 0.6 g; Protein 27.7 g; Carbohydrate 47.4 g; Fiber 4.1 g; Cholesterol 68 mg

spicy fish kabobs

Cooked on skewers, these low-fat spicy fish kebobs are a great way to make fish more appealing and easy to eat.

2 lb 4 oz (1 kg) firm white boneless fish fillets *(see Hint)*

1 cup (9 oz/250 g) low-fat plain yogurt

2 garlic cloves, crushed

1 tsp chopped fresh ginger

1 red chili, finely chopped

2 tsp garam masala

1 tbs chopped cilantro (coriander) leaves

canola or olive oil spray

wholegrain bread, to serve

Prep time: 15 minutes + 1 hour marinating

Cooking time: 10 minutes

Serves 6

Soak 12 wooden skewers for 30 minutes. Cut the fish into 1¼ in (3 cm) cubes.

To make the marinade, mix the yogurt, garlic, ginger, chili, garam masala and cilantro in a small bowl.

Thread the fish onto skewers and put in a shallow non-metallic dish. Spoon the marinade over the fish, cover and marinate in the refrigerator for 1 hour.

Preheat the broiler (grill) or barbecue to high and lightly spray the grill with oil. Broil or barbecue the skewers for 5–6 minutes, turning occasionally. The fish is cooked when it flakes easily when tested with a fork. Serve with the bread and a green salad.

HINTS: Try wahoo, cod, bream or ocean perch.

You could try this recipe with vegetable pilaf (see page 186).

nutrition per serving Energy 199 Cal (838 kJ); Fat 4.3 g; Saturated fat 1.3 g; Protein 36.7 g; Carbohydrate 2.9 g; Fiber 0.3 g; Cholesterol 100 mg

barbecued asian-style shrimp

After tasting this delicious dish, everyone will want more. Shrimp provide plenty of protein with relatively few calories—a great choice for those watching their weight.

14 oz (400 g) can cannellini beans, drained and rinsed

10½ oz (300 g) can chickpeas, drained and rinsed

11 oz (310 g) can corn kernels, drained and rinsed

1 tsp grated lime zest

2 tbs chopped cilantro (coriander) leaves

1 lb 2 oz (500 g) large raw shrimp (prawns)

2 tbs lemon juice

1 tbs sesame oil

2 garlic cloves, crushed

2 tsp grated fresh ginger

canola or olive oil spray

lime quarters, to serve

Prep time: 10 minutes + 3 hours marinating

Cooking time: 5 minutes

Serves 4

Combine the cannellini beans, chickpeas and corn kernels in a large bowl. Stir through the lime zest and cilantro.

Peel the shrimp, leaving the tails intact. Gently pull out the dark vein from each shrimp back, starting at the head end.

To make the marinade, combine the lemon juice, sesame oil, garlic and ginger in a small bowl. Add the shrimp and gently stir to coat them in the marinade. Cover and refrigerate for at least 3 hours.

Heat a barbecue hotplate until hot. Spray the hotplate with oil, then cook the shrimp for 3–5 minutes, or until pink and cooked through. Brush frequently with marinade while cooking. Serve immediately with the bean mixture and wedges of lime.

HINT: Alternatively, the shrimp can be threaded onto bamboo skewers. Soak the skewers in cold water for about 30 minutes. This will prevent the skewers burning during cooking. After marinating, thread the shrimp evenly onto the skewers and cook as stated, turning and basting occasionally during cooking.

nutrition per serving Energy 263 Cal (1103 kJ); Fat 7.5 g; Saturated fat 1.1 g; Protein 23 g; Carbohydrate 25.6 g; Fiber 8.7 g; Cholesterol 93 mg

corn and bacon crustless quiches

Impress your friends with these reduced-fat quiches—all the flavor but less fat than regular quiches.

4 corn cobs

1 tsp olive oil

4 slices low-fat bacon (we used 97% fat-free), cut into thin strips

1 small onion, finely chopped

3 eggs, lightly beaten

2 tbs chopped chives

2 tbs chopped parsley

¾ cup (2¼ oz/60 g) fresh wholegrain breadcrumbs

4 tbs skim or non-fat evaporated milk

Prep time: 30 minutes

Cooking time: 40 minutes

Makes 4

Preheat the oven to 350°F (180°C/Gas 4). Lightly grease four ¾ cup (6 fl oz/185 ml) ramekins. Remove the husks from the corn and, using a coarse grater, grate the corn kernels into a deep bowl. There should be about 1½ cups corn flesh and juice.

Heat the oil in a frying pan and cook the bacon and onion for 3–4 minutes, or until the onion softens. Add to the corn in the bowl. Stir in the eggs, chives, parsley, breadcrumbs and evaporated milk and season well with salt and freshly ground black pepper. Spoon into the ramekins.

Put the ramekins in a large baking dish. Add enough hot water to come halfway up the sides of the ramekins. Lay foil loosely over the top. Bake for 25–30 minutes, or until just set.

nutrition per serving Energy 269 Cal (1124 kJ); Fat 7.8 g; Saturated fat 1.9 g; Protein 18.8 g; Carbohydrate 31.5 g; Fiber 7 g; Cholesterol 172 mg

scallops and vegetables with dressing

This dish gets top marks for flavor and good nutrition—it's a good source of protein and beta-carotene, and provides a range of minerals.

16 large scallops, in shells

canola or olive oil spray

2 tsp olive oil

2 scallions (spring onions), finely chopped

4 slices low-fat bacon (we used 97% fat-free), finely chopped

½ small red pepper (capsicum), seeded and finely diced

½ celery stalk, finely diced

1 tbs finely chopped parsley

3½ oz (100 g) mixed salad leaves

2¼ oz (60 g) snow pea (mangetout) sprouts, trimmed and blanched

1 scallion (spring onion), cut into thin shreds, to garnish

3 tbs fat-free balsamic or French dressing

Prep time: 30 minutes

Cooking time: 10 minutes

Serves 4

Slice or pull off any vein, membrane or hard white muscle from the scallops, leaving any roe attached. Gently pat dry with paper towels. Put on a large baking sheet in their shells and lightly spray the scallops with oil. Preheat the broiler (grill).

Heat the oil in a frying pan. Add the scallion and bacon, cook for 2 minutes, then add the pepper and celery. Cook, stirring frequently for 3 minutes, or until the vegetables are softened. Add the parsley and season well with salt and freshly ground black pepper.

Broil the scallops for 1–2 minutes, taking care not to overcook. Arrange four shells around the outside of four large plates. Spoon some warm vegetable mixture over each scallop. Divide the mixed salad leaves and snow pea sprouts into four portions and put some in the center of each plate. Garnish the salad with the scallion shreds. Drizzle a little dressing over the scallops and the salad. Serve immediately.

HINT: You can reduce the GI of this salad further by using diet fat-free salad dressing that contains non-nutritive sweetener instead of sugar.

nutrition per serving Energy 130 Cal (546 kJ); Fat 4.2 g; Saturated fat 0.5 g; Protein 14.8 g; Carbohydrate 9 g; Fiber 1.8 g; Cholesterol 21 mg

fresh rice noodles with garlic and ginger shrimp

This recipe is full of freshness and bursting with flavor. It is very easy to make, completely satisfying and low in fat.

2 lb 4 oz (1 kg) raw jumbo shrimp (king prawns)

14 oz (400 g) fresh rice noodles

2 tsp canola oil

3–4 garlic cloves, finely chopped

2 in (5 cm) piece fresh ginger, cut into matchsticks

2–3 small red chilies, seeded and finely chopped

6 cilantro (coriander) roots, finely chopped, plus a few leaves to garnish

8 scallions (spring onions), cut into short lengths

½ red pepper (capsicum), thinly sliced

2 tbs lemon juice

½ cup (4 fl oz/125 ml) white wine

1 tsp crushed jaggery (palm sugar) or soft brown sugar

2 tsp fish sauce

Prep time: 25 minutes
Cooking time: 20 minutes
Serves 4

Peel the shrimp, leaving the tails intact. Gently pull out the dark vein from each shrimp back, starting at the head end.

Put the noodles in a large heatproof bowl, cover with boiling water and soak for 8 minutes, or until softened. Separate gently and drain.

Heat a wok until very hot, add the oil and swirl to coat. Stir-fry the shrimp, garlic, ginger, chili and cilantro root in two batches for 1–2 minutes over high heat, or until the shrimp turn pink. Remove the shrimp from the wok and set aside.

Add the scallion and pepper to the wok. Cook over high heat for 2–3 minutes. Add the lemon juice, wine and jaggery. Cook until the liquid has reduced by two-thirds.

Add the shrimp and sprinkle with fish sauce. Toss to heat through. Garnish with cilantro leaves and serve with the noodles.

nutrition per serving Energy 368 Cal (1542 kJ); Fat 4.3 g; Saturated fat 0.3 g; Protein 31 g; Carbohydrate 45 g; Fiber 3 g; Cholesterol 186 mg

noodles with beef

This dish is a great choice for people who need to eat more iron. It is a good source of well-absorbed iron, zinc and B-group vitamins.

1 lb 2 oz (500 g) fresh rice noodle sheets

canola oil spray

2 eggs, lightly beaten

2 tsp peanut oil

1 lb 2 oz (500 g) lean rump steak, trimmed and thinly sliced across the grain

3 tbs kecap manis

1½ tbs soy sauce

1½ tbs fish sauce

10½ oz (300 g) Chinese kale (gai larn), cut into 2 in (5 cm) lengths

¼ tsp ground white pepper

lemon wedges, to serve

Prep time: 20 minutes

Cooking time: 20 minutes

Serves 4–6

Cut the noodle sheets lengthwise into ¾ in (2 cm) strips. Put the noodles in a large heatproof bowl, cover with boiling water and soak for 8 minutes, or until softened, then gently separate the strips and drain.

Heat a wok over medium heat, and spray with oil. Add the egg, swirl to coat and cook for 1–2 minutes, or until set. Remove, roll up and cut into shreds.

Reheat the wok over high heat, add the peanut oil and swirl to coat. Stir-fry the beef in batches for 3 minutes, or until browned. Remove from the wok.

Reduce the heat to medium, add the noodles and stir-fry for 2 minutes. Combine the kecap manis, soy sauce and fish sauce. Add to the wok with the kale and white pepper, then stir-fry for a further 2 minutes. Return the egg and beef to the wok and stir-fry for another 3 minutes, or until the kale has wilted and the noodles are soft but not falling apart. Serve with the lemon wedges on the side.

HINTS: Rice noodles should not be refrigerated, since they are very difficult to work with. Use precut fresh rice noodles if sheets are not available.

Kecap manis is an Indonesian sauce similar to a sweet tasting soy sauce. It is available in most supermarkets and Asian markets.

nutrition per serving (6) Energy 318 Cal (1334 kJ); Fat 7.9 g; Saturated fat 2.5 g; Protein 25.7 g; Carbohydrate 35.3 g; Fiber 2.4 g; Cholesterol 116 mg

stir-fried fresh tuna and green beans with rice

Not only is this meal delicious, but it's also a good source of healthy omega-3 fats, antioxidants, folate and potassium.

2 cups (14 oz/400 g) basmati rice, rinsed and drained

10½ oz (300 g) small green beans, trimmed

2 tsp canola oil

1 lb 5 oz (600 g) fresh tuna, cut into small cubes

9 oz (250 g) small cherry tomatoes

16 small black olives

2–3 tbs lemon juice

2 garlic cloves, finely chopped

8 anchovy fillets in brine, drained and finely chopped

1 handful small basil leaves

Prep time: 25 minutes

Cooking time: 30 minutes

Serves 4

Put the rice and 4 cups (35 fl oz/1 liter) water in a saucepan and bring to a boil over medium heat. Reduce the heat to low, cover with a lid and cook for 20 minutes, or until the rice is tender. Remove from the heat and leave to stand, covered, for 5 minutes.

Bring a small saucepan of water to a boil. Add the beans and cook for 2 minutes. Drain and refresh under very cold water so they keep their color. Set aside.

Heat a wok until very hot, add the oil and swirl to coat. Stir-fry the tuna for about 5 minutes, or until it is cooked on the outside, but still pink in the middle.

Add the cherry tomatoes, olives and beans and gently toss until heated through. Stir in the lemon juice, garlic and anchovies. Season with salt and freshly ground black pepper and serve sprinkled with the basil leaves. Serve with the rice.

nutrition per serving Energy 652 Cal (2739 kJ); Fat 12.2 g; Saturated fat 4 g; Protein 48.6 g; Carbohydrate 85.9 g; Fiber 4.4 g; Cholesterol 60 mg

spicy chicken burgers

These chicken burgers are easy to make and are a much healthier alternative to regular take-away burgers.

1 lb 2 oz (500 g) lean ground (minced) chicken

4 scallions (spring onions), finely chopped

4 tbs finely chopped fresh cilantro (coriander) leaves

2 garlic cloves, crushed

¼ tsp cayenne pepper

1 egg white, lightly beaten

1 tbs olive or canola oil

1 lemon, halved

5½ oz (150 g) tabbouleh (see recipe on page 72)

4 wholegrain bread rolls, halved

Prep time: 10 minutes + 20 minutes refrigeration
Cooking time: 10 minutes
Serves 4

Mix together the chicken, scallion, cilantro, garlic, cayenne pepper and egg white and season with salt and freshly ground black pepper. Shape the mixture into four patties. Refrigerate for 20 minutes before cooking.

Heat the oil in a large non-stick frying pan over medium heat, add the patties and cook for about 5 minutes on each side, or until browned and cooked through.

Squeeze the lemon on the cooked patties and drain well on paper towels. Add the patties to the halved wholegrain buns and fill with the tabbouleh.

nutrition per serving Energy 426 Cal (1789 kJ); Fat 19.2 g; Saturated fat 3.9 g; Protein 31.4 g; Carbohydrate 32.1 g; Fiber 5.6 g; Cholesterol 113 mg

pasta siracusani

This Mediterranean-style dish is a good source of antioxidants. If you're watching your weight use whole wheat (wholemeal) spaghetti because it will stave off hunger for longer, as well as provide extra fiber.

2 tsp olive oil

2 garlic cloves, crushed

1 large green pepper (capsicum), thinly sliced

2 x 14 oz (400 g) cans chopped tomatoes

2 zucchini (courgettes), chopped

2 anchovy fillets in brine, drained and chopped

1 tbs capers, chopped

3 tbs black olives in brine, pitted and halved

2 tbs chopped basil

1 lb 2 oz (500 g) spaghetti or linguine

⅔ cup (2¼ oz/60 g) grated Parmesan cheese

Prep time: 20 minutes

Cooking time: 30 minutes

Serves 4–6

Heat the oil in a large, deep frying pan and cook the garlic for 30 seconds over low heat. Add the peppers, tomatoes, zucchini, anchovies, capers, olives and ½ cup (4 fl oz/125 ml) water. Cook for 20 minutes, stirring occasionally.

Add the basil to the pan and stir well. Season to taste with salt and freshly ground black pepper.

Meanwhile, cook the pasta in a large saucepan of boiling water for 10 minutes, or until *al dente*. Drain well. Serve the pasta topped with the sauce and grated Parmesan.

The longer pasta is cooked the more digestible its carbohydrate becomes and the higher its GI value. Protein-enriched pasta has a slightly lower GI value than regular pasta.

nutrition per serving (6) Energy 362 Cal (1522 kJ); Fat 5.3 g; Saturated fat 1.9 g; Protein 14.2 g; Carbohydrate 63.7 g; Fiber 5.4 g; Cholesterol 8 mg

marinated chili squid

To save preparation time, you can marinate the squid overnight or during the day and cook in the evening. Serve it on its own as a starter or with fresh rice noodles for a complete low-GI meal.

1 lb 2 oz (500 g) cleaned squid hoods

1 tbs finely chopped fresh ginger

2–3 small red chilies, finely chopped

3 garlic cloves, finely chopped

1 tbs canola oil

canola oil spray

2 onions, thinly sliced

1 lb 2 oz (500 g) baby bok choy, washed and roughly chopped

Prep time: 10 minutes + 3 hours marinating
Cooking time: 15 minutes
Serves 4

Wash the squid well and pat dry with paper towels. Cut into ½ in (1 cm) rings and put in a shallow non-metallic bowl. Combine the ginger, chili, garlic and oil, pour over the rings and toss well. Cover and refrigerate for 2–3 hours, or overnight.

Drain the rings, reserving the marinade. Heat a wok until very hot and spray with oil.

Stir-fry the rings over high heat in batches for 1–2 minutes. Remove from the wok as soon as the squid turns white, being careful not to overcook it or it will become rubbery.

Heat the reserved marinade in the wok. Add the onion and cook over medium heat for 3–4 minutes, or until it is slightly softened. Add the bok choy and cook, covered, for 2 minutes, or until it has wilted slightly. Return the rings to the wok and toss until well combined. Season well with salt and freshly ground black pepper. Remove from the wok and serve immediately

HINTS: Reheat the wok between cooking batches of rings otherwise the flesh will be tough.

For a main meal, serve with 14 oz (400 g) fresh rice noodles. To cook the noodles, put them in a large heatproof bowl, cover with boiling water and soak for 8 minutes, or until softened. Separate gently and drain.

nutrition per serving Energy 175 Cal (733 kJ); Fat 7 g; Saturated fat 0.9 g; Protein 23.3 g; Carbohydrate 4.7 g; Fiber 2.9 g; Cholesterol 249 mg

penne with bacon, ricotta and basil sauce

Delicious freshly prepared or served as leftovers, this Italian meal is rich in flavor and nutrients.

2 tsp olive oil

4 slices low-fat bacon (we used 97% fat-free), chopped

2–3 garlic cloves, crushed

1 onion, finely chopped

2 scallions (spring onions), finely chopped

1 cup (9 oz/250 g) low-fat ricotta cheese

3 handfuls basil, finely chopped, plus extra whole leaves, to garnish

11½ oz (325 g) penne

12 cherry tomatoes, halved

Prep time: 20 minutes
Cooking time: 15 minutes
Serves 4

Heat the oil in a frying pan, add the bacon, garlic, onion and scallions and stir over medium heat for 5 minutes, or until cooked. Remove from the heat, stir in the ricotta and chopped basil and beat until smooth.

Cook the pasta in a large saucepan of boiling water for 10 minutes, or until *al dente*. Just prior to draining the pasta, add about 1 cup (9 fl oz/250 ml) of the pasta cooking water to the ricotta mixture to thin the sauce. Add more water if you prefer an even thinner sauce. Season with salt and freshly ground black pepper.

Drain the pasta and stir the ricotta sauce and tomato halves through the pasta. Garnish with extra basil.

nutrition per serving Energy 412 Cal (1731 kJ); Fat 9.5 g; Saturated fat 4 g; Protein 21.8 g; Carbohydrate 60.3 g; Fiber 4.6 g; Cholesterol 26 mg

fusilli with tuna, capers and parsley

This recipe combines two popular foods, tuna and pasta, to make a nourishing flavor-packed meal. A great choice for a weeknight dinner.

15 oz (425 g) can tuna in brine or spring water, drained

1 tbs olive oil

2 garlic cloves, finely chopped

2 small red chilies, finely chopped

3 tbs capers

2 large handfuls Italian (flat-leaf) parsley, chopped

3 tbs lemon juice

13 oz (375 g) fusilli

Prep time: 15 minutes
Cooking time: 10 minutes
Serves 4

Put the drained tuna in a bowl and flake lightly with a fork. In a small bowl, combine the oil, garlic, chili, capers, parsley and lemon juice. Pour over the tuna and mix lightly. Season well with salt and freshly ground black pepper.

Meanwhile, cook the pasta in a large saucepan of boiling water for 10 minutes, or until *al dente*. Just prior to draining the pasta, reserve ½ cup (4 fl oz/125 ml) of the pasta cooking water. Drain the pasta. Toss the tuna mixture through the pasta, adding the reserved pasta water. Serve immediately.

nutrition per serving Energy 457 Cal (1912 kJ); Fat 7.0 g; Saturated fat 1.5 g; Protein 29.3 g; Carbohydrate 65.6 g; Fiber 4 g; Cholesterol 39 mg

fettuccine boscaiola

This vegetarian pasta dish is ready in no time at all and is a great everyday meal. It's low in fat and will give you good amounts of folate and beta-carotene.

1 lb 2 oz (500 g) button mushrooms

2 tsp olive oil

1 large onion, roughly chopped

2 garlic cloves, finely chopped

2 x 14 oz (400 g) cans chopped tomatoes

1 lb 2 oz (500 g) fettuccine

2 tbs chopped parsley

Prep time: 20 minutes
Cooking time: 30 minutes
Serves 6

Wipe the mushrooms with a damp paper towel, then slice the caps and stems finely.

Heat the oil in a heavy-based frying pan and cook the onion and garlic over medium heat, stirring occasionally, for about 6 minutes, or until the vegetables are light golden. Add the tomato and mushrooms to the pan and bring the mixture to a boil. Reduce the heat, cover the pan and simmer for 15 minutes.

Meanwhile, cook the fettuccine in a large saucepan of boiling water for 10 minutes, or until *al dente*. Drain and return to the pan.

Stir the parsley into the sauce and season well with salt and freshly ground black pepper. Toss the sauce through the pasta. Serve with a mixed green salad.

nutrition per serving Energy 359 Cal (1508 kJ); Fat 3.3 g; Saturated fat 0.5 g; Protein 15.3 g; Carbohydrate 65.9 g; Fiber 6.5 g; Cholesterol 15 mg

pasta puttanesca

This spicy pasta dish makes a delicious and lively meal—it's good enough to enjoy with company or to eat on your own.

2 tsp olive oil

3 garlic cloves, crushed

2 tbs chopped parsley

¼–½ tsp chili flakes or powder

2 x 14 oz (400 g) cans chopped tomatoes

1 lb 2 oz (500 g) spaghetti

1 tbs capers

3 anchovy fillets in brine, drained and thinly sliced

¼ cup (1½ oz/40 g) black olives in brine, drained, pitted and chopped

Prep time: 20 minutes

Cooking time: 25 minutes

Serves 4

Heat the oil in a large heavy-based frying pan. Add the garlic, parsley and chili flakes and stir constantly for about 1 minute over medium heat. Add the tomato to the pan and bring to a boil. Reduce the heat and simmer, covered, for 10 minutes.

Meanwhile, cook the pasta in a large saucepan of boiling water for 10 minutes, or until *al dente*. Drain and return to the pan.

Add the capers, anchovies and olives to the tomato mixture and stir for another 5 minutes. Season with freshly ground black pepper. Add the sauce to the pasta and toss gently. Serve with a green salad.

nutrition per serving Energy 490 Cal (2056 kJ); Fat 4.4 g; Saturated fat 0.6 g; Protein 16.6 g; Carbohydrate 94.5 g; Fiber 7.2 g; Cholesterol 2 mg

A nourishing, healthy dinner is essential for maintaining good health in the long term. Along with regular exercise, our bodies need a wide range of nutrients in certain amounts to work properly and stay healthy. The recipes in this chapter provide you with main meals that provide low-GI carbohydrates and lean protein-rich foods, such as meat, poultry, fish and seafood to nourish the heartiest of appetites.

main meals

rigatoni with kidney beans and sausage

This recipe proves how easy it can be to include legumes in your diet.

2 tsp olive oil

1 large onion, chopped

2 garlic cloves, crushed

4 lean beef sausages

2 x 14 oz (400 g) cans tomatoes

14 oz (400 g) can red kidney beans, drained and rinsed

2 tbs chopped basil

1 tbs chopped sage

1 tbs chopped parsley

1 lb 2 oz (500 g) rigatoni

grated Parmesan cheese (optional), to serve

Prep time: 25 minutes

Cooking time: 35 minutes

Serves 4–6

Heat the oil in a saucepan over medium heat. Add the onion, garlic and sausage and cook, stirring occasionally, for 5 minutes. Remove the sausages, chop and return to the saucepan.

Add the tomato, beans, basil, sage and parsley and season well with salt and freshly ground black pepper. Reduce the heat and simmer for 20 minutes.

Meanwhile, cook the pasta in a large saucepan of boiling water for 10 minutes, or until *al dente*. Drain well. Divide among bowls and top with the sauce. If you like, sprinkle with Parmesan before serving.

HINTS: If you prefer, you can use dried beans instead of the canned ones. Soak them overnight in water, then drain, transfer to a saucepan, cover well with water and boil for 20 minutes, or until tender.

Any large pasta shape will work well.

Any leftovers can be frozen or stored in the refrigerator for up to 3 days.

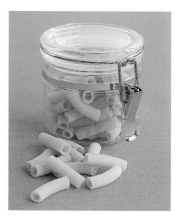

nutrition per serving (6) Energy 431 Cal (1809 kJ); Fat 9.2 g; Saturated fat 1.8 g; Protein 20 g; Carbohydrate 71.5 g; Fiber 7.8 g; Cholesterol 30 mg

mongolian hot pot

Hot Pots are a great way to include a variety of healthy foods in one meal. This spicy dish provides a satisfying and nutritious low-GI meal.

14 oz (400 g) fresh rice noodles

1 lb 5 oz (600 g) lean lamb loin or tenderloin (fillet)

4 scallions (spring onions), sliced

6 cups (52 fl oz/1.5 liters) chicken stock

6 thin slices fresh ginger

2 tbs Chinese rice wine

10½ oz (300 g) silken firm tofu, cut into ⅝ in (1.5 cm) cubes

10½ oz (300 g) Chinese kale (gai larn), cut into 1½ in (4 cm) lengths

3 cups (5½ oz/150 g) shredded Chinese cabbage

SAUCE

4 tbs light soy sauce

2 tbs Chinese sesame paste

1 tbs Chinese rice wine

1 tsp chili and garlic paste

Prep time: 20 minutes
Cooking time: 5 minutes
Serves 6

Put the noodles in a large heatproof bowl, cover with boiling water and soak for 8 minutes, or until softened. Separate gently and drain. Divide among 6 bowls.

Trim the lamb, then thinly slice across the grain. Divide the lamb strips among the bowls, then add the scallion.

Pour the stock into a 10 cup (87 fl oz/2.5 liter) flameproof hotchpotch or large saucepan, then add the ginger and rice wine. Cover and bring to a boil over high heat. Add the tofu, Chinese kale and Chinese cabbage and simmer, uncovered, for 1 minute, or until the broccoli has wilted.

To make the sauce, combine the soy sauce, sesame paste, rice wine and chili and garlic paste in a small bowl.

Divide the tofu, broccoli and cabbage among the bowls, then ladle on the hot stock—it will be hot enough to cook the lamb. Drizzle a little of the sauce on top and serve the rest on the side.

nutrition per serving Energy 396 Cal (1665 kJ); Fat 12.7 g; Saturated fat 3.1 g; Protein 35.8 g; Carbohydrate 32.6 g; Fiber 5.3 g; Cholesterol 65 mg

rice noodles with fish and black beans

This hearty meal combines the filling powers of fish protein and low-GI carbohydrate to provide you with a sustaining and nutritious meal—a great choice for those watching their weight.

14 oz (400 g) fresh rice noodles

7 oz (200 g) Chinese kale (gai larn), cut into 2 in (5 cm) lengths

2 tbs light soy sauce

1½ tbs Chinese rice wine

½ tsp sesame oil

1 tsp cornstarch (cornflour)

1 lb 4 oz (550 g) skinless white fish fillets

2 tsp canola oil

5 garlic cloves, crushed

2 tsp finely chopped ginger

2 scallions (spring onions), finely chopped, plus extra, thinly sliced on the diagonal, to garnish

2 small red chilies, finely chopped

2 tbs canned salted black beans, rinsed, roughly chopped

⅔ cup (5½ fl oz/170 ml) fish stock

Put the noodles in a large heatproof bowl, cover with boiling water and soak for 8 minutes, or until softened. Separate gently and drain.

Put the Chinese broccoli in a steamer, cover and steam over a wok or large saucepan of simmering water for 2 minutes, or until slightly wilted. Remove from the heat and keep warm.

To make the marinade, combine the soy sauce, rice wine, sesame oil and cornstarch in a large non-metallic bowl. Cut the fish into 1½ in (4 cm) pieces, checking for bones. Add to the marinade and toss to coat well.

Heat a wok over high heat, add the canola oil and swirl to coat. Add the garlic, ginger, scallion, chili and black beans and stir-fry for 1 minute. Add the fish and marinade and cook for 2 minutes, or until the fish is almost cooked through. Remove the fish with a slotted spoon and keep warm. Add the stock to the wok and bring to a boil. Reduce the heat to low and bring to a simmer. Cook for 5 minutes, or until the sauce has slightly thickened. Return the fish to the wok, cover with a lid and simmer gently for 2–3 minutes, or until just cooked.

Divide the noodles among four plates, top with the Chinese broccoli and spoon the fish and black bean sauce on top. Garnish with the extra scallion.

Prep time: 20 minutes

Cooking time: 20 minutes

Serves 4

nutrition per serving Energy 345 Cal (1448 kJ); Fat 5.7 g; Saturated fat 0.9 g; Protein 24.6 g; Carbohydrate 46.5 g; Fiber 3.6 g; Cholesterol 54 mg

spaghetti with meatballs

This classic recipe is a family favorite. If you have diabetes, use protein-enriched spaghetti for an even lower GI meal.

1 lb 2 oz (500 g) lean ground (minced) beef

½ cup (1½ oz/40 g) fresh wholegrain breadcrumbs

1 small onion, finely chopped

2 garlic cloves, crushed

2 tsp worcestershire sauce

1 tsp dried oregano

¼ cup (1 oz/30 g) all-purpose (plain) flour

1 tbs olive oil

1 lb 2 oz (500 g) spaghetti

SAUCE

2 x 14 oz (400 g) cans chopped tomatoes

1 tsp olive oil

1 onion, finely chopped

2 garlic cloves, crushed

2 tbs tomato paste

½ cup (4 fl oz/125 ml) beef stock

Prep time: 30 minutes

Cooking time: 40 minutes

Serves 4

To make the meatballs, combine the beef, breadcrumbs, onion, garlic, worcestershire sauce and oregano in a bowl and season to taste with salt and freshly ground black pepper. Use your hands to mix the ingredients together well. Roll level tablespoons of the mixture into balls, dust lightly with the flour and shake off the excess.

Heat the oil in a deep frying pan and cook the meatballs in batches, turning frequently, until browned all over. Drain well on paper towels. Wipe the pan out with paper towels.

To make the sauce, purée the tomatoes in a food processor or blender. Heat the oil in the frying pan. Add the onion and cook over medium heat for 2–3 minutes, or until soft and just lightly golden. Add the garlic and cook for a further 1 minute. Add the puréed tomatoes, tomato paste and stock to the pan and stir to combine. Bring the mixture to a boil, then add the meatballs. Reduce the heat and simmer for 15 minutes, turning the meatballs once. Season with pepper.

Meanwhile, cook the spaghetti in a large saucepan of boiling water for 10 minutes, or until *al dente*. Drain, divide among four plates and top with the meatballs and sauce. Great with a mixed green salad.

nutrition per serving Energy 760 Cal (3192 kJ); Fat 16.7 g; Saturated fat 4.8 g; Protein 44.4 g; Carbohydrate 106.8 g; Fiber 9 g; Cholesterol 64 mg

chicken, white bean and zucchini stew

This recipe is great to make in a big batch on the weekend and serve into individual portions. These can then be kept in the freezer for up to 1 month and reheated for a quick and easy meal.

2 tsp olive oil

8 skinless chicken thigh cutlets, trimmed

1 onion, thinly sliced

4 garlic cloves, finely chopped

3 tbs white wine

1 cup (9 fl oz/250 ml) chicken stock

1 tbs finely chopped rosemary

1 tsp grated lemon zest

1 bay leaf

2 x 14 oz (400 g) cans cannellini beans, drained and rinsed

3 zucchini (courgettes), halved lengthwise, then sliced on the diagonal

13 oz (375 g) fusilli

Prep time: 20 minutes

Cooking time: 1 hour 10 minutes

Serves 4

Heat the oil in a large flameproof casserole. Add the chicken in batches and cook for 4 minutes on each side, or until browned. Remove the chicken.

Add the onion and cook for 5 minutes, or until softened. Add the garlic and cook for 1 minute, or until fragrant, then pour in the wine and stock and bring to a boil, scraping the bottom of the pan to remove any sediment.

Return the chicken and any juices to the pan along with the rosemary, lemon zest and bay leaf. Reduce the heat and simmer, covered, for 40 minutes, or until the chicken is tender. Stir in the cannellini beans and zucchini and cook for a further 5 minutes, or until the zucchini is tender.

Meanwhile, cook the pasta in a large saucepan of boiling water for 10 minutes, or until *al dente*. Drain and serve with the chicken.

nutrition per serving Energy 772 Cal (3244 kJ); Fat 19.9 g; Saturated fat 5.5 g; Protein 62.9 g; Carbohydrate 84.4 g; Fiber 13.7 g; Cholesterol 188 mg

warm shrimp and scallop stir-fry

Seafood lovers will enjoy this dish. The lemon sauce and vegetables complement the delicate texture of the scallops, and add color and nutrients.

2 cups (14 oz/400 g) basmati rice, rinsed and drained

1 lb 2 oz (500 g) raw shrimp (prawns)

10½ oz (300 g) scallops

2 tsp five-spice powder

1–2 small fresh red chilies, seeded and finely chopped

2–3 garlic cloves, crushed

2 tsp sesame oil

7 oz (200 g) asparagus, trimmed and cut into short lengths

5½ oz (150 g) snow peas (mangetout), trimmed

4½ oz (125 g) arugula (rocket), torn into pieces

2 tbs light soy sauce

2 tbs lemon juice

1 tbs mirin

2 tsp honey

6 scallions (spring onions), chopped

1 tbs chopped cilantro (coriander) leaves

1 tbs sesame seeds, toasted

Prep time: 30 minutes + 10 minutes marinating

Cooking time: 35 minutes

Serves 4

Put the rice and 4 cups (35 fl oz/1 liter) water in a saucepan and bring to a boil over medium heat. Reduce the heat to low, cover with a lid and cook for 20 minutes, or until the rice is tender. Remove from the heat and leave to stand, covered, for 5 minutes.

Meanwhile, prepare the seafood. Peel the shrimp, leaving the tails intact. Gently pull out the dark vein from each shrimp back, starting at the head end. Slice or pull off any vein, membrane or hard white muscle from the scallops, leaving any roe attached. Combine the five-spice powder, chili, garlic and sesame oil in a large non-metallic bowl. Add the shrimp and scallops and toss to coat. Cover with plastic wrap and refrigerate for at least 10 minutes.

Blanch the asparagus and snow peas briefly in a saucepan of boiling water. Drain and plunge into a bowl of ice water, then drain again. Arrange the asparagus, snow peas and arugula on four plates.

Combine the soy sauce, lemon juice, mirin and honey in a small bowl.

Heat a wok over high heat, add the shrimp, scallops and scallion in batches and cook for 3–4 minutes, or until cooked through. Remove from the wok and set aside. Reheat the wok between batches.

Add the soy–lemon sauce and cilantro to the wok, and bring to a boil. Cook over high heat for 1–2 minutes. Return the seafood to the wok and toss well. Divide among the plates and sprinkle with the sesame seeds. Serve with the rice.

nutrition per serving Energy 545 Cal (2291 kJ); Fat 5.8 g; Saturated fat 0.8 g; Protein 33.2 g; Carbohydrate 88.7 g; Fiber 4.7 g; Cholesterol 118 mg

cilantro beef with noodles

Prepare the marinade in the morning, then allow the flavors to develop over time. The lime juice and cilantro give a tangy flavor boost.

4 garlic cloves, finely chopped

1 tbs finely chopped fresh ginger

1 large handful cilantro (coriander) roots, stems and leaves, chopped

3 tsp canola oil

1 lb 2 oz (500 g) lean beef tip steak

14 oz (400 g) fresh rice noodles

canola oil spray

1 red onion, thinly sliced

½ red pepper (capsicum), thinly sliced

½ green pepper (capsicum), thinly sliced

2 tbs lime juice

2 tbs reduced-salt soy sauce

1 large handful cilantro (coriander) leaves, extra

Prep time: 20 minutes + 2 hours marinating
Cooking time: 20 minutes
Serves 4

To make the marinade, combine the garlic, ginger, cilantro and 2 teaspoons of the oil in a large non-metallic bowl. Trim the beef, then cut into thin strips across the grain. Add to the marinade and toss to coat. Cover with plastic wrap and refrigerate for 2 hours, or overnight.

Put the rice noodles in a large heatproof bowl, cover with boiling water and soak for 8 minutes, or until softened. Separate gently and drain.

Heat a wok until very hot over high heat and spray with the oil. Add the meat in three batches and stir-fry for 2–3 minutes, or until the meat is just cooked. Remove all the meat from the wok and keep it warm. Reheat and respray the wok between batches.

Heat the remaining 1 teaspoon oil in the wok, add the onion and cook over medium heat for 3–4 minutes, or until slightly softened. Add the pepper and cook, tossing constantly, for 3–4 minutes, or until slightly softened.

Return all the meat to the wok along with the lime juice, soy sauce, 2 tablespoons water and extra cilantro. Add the noodles. Toss well, then remove from the heat and season well with salt and freshly ground black pepper.

nutrition per serving Energy 406 Cal (1701 kJ); Fat 10 g; Saturated fat 2.8 g; Protein 32.6 g; Carbohydrate 44.3 g; Fiber 2.2 g; Cholesterol 80 mg

ginger chili fish cutlets
with cilantro rice

Ready in a flash—this dish is great when you want to eat healthy meals but have little time for cooking. This is a good source of protein.

2 cups (14 oz/400 g) basmati rice, rinsed and drained

4 firm white fish cutlets (*see Hints*)

2 in (5 cm) piece fresh ginger, shredded

2 garlic cloves, chopped

2 tsp chopped red chili

2 tbs chopped cilantro (coriander) stems and leaves

3 scallions (spring onions), finely shredded

extra cilantro (coriander) leaves, chopped

3 tbs lime juice

1 tbs fish sauce

2 tsp honey

Prep time: 20 minutes
Cooking time: 30 minutes
Serves 4

Put the rice and 4 cups (35 fl oz/1 liter) water in a saucepan and bring to a boil over medium heat. Reduce the heat to low, cover with a lid and cook for 20 minutes, or until the rice is tender. Remove from the heat and leave to stand, covered, for 5 minutes.

Line a large bamboo steamer basket with banana leaves or baking paper.

Arrange the fish in the basket and top with the ginger, garlic, chili and cilantro stems and leaves. Cover and steam over a wok or large saucepan of boiling water for 8–10 minutes. Sprinkle the scallion over the fish. Cover and steam for 30 seconds, or until the fish flakes easily with a fork. Stir the extra cilantro leaves into the rice. Divide the rice onto serving plates. Top with the fish and pour over the combined lime juice, fish sauce and honey.

HINTS: Try snapper, catfish or cod.

To lower the GI further, you can dilute the rice with boiled or canned lentils.

nutrition per serving Energy 534 Cal (2236 kJ); Fat 3.2 g; Saturated fat 1.1 g; Protein 39.7 g; Carbohydrate 84.1 g; Fiber 1.6 g; Cholesterol 96 mg

paella

This colorful Spanish dish is as nutritious as it is delicious.

12 raw shrimp (prawns)

12–16 black mussels

3½ oz (100 g) skinless firm white fish fillet

1 small skinless, boneless chicken breast

1 ripe tomato

½ cup (4 fl oz/125 ml) dry white wine

1½ small red onions, finely chopped

2 tbs olive oil

3½ oz (100 g) squid rings

2 slices low-fat bacon (97% fat-free), chopped

4 garlic cloves, crushed

1 small red pepper (capsicum), finely chopped

3¼ oz (90 g) thin lean cooked beef sausages, thinly sliced

pinch of cayenne pepper

1 cup (7 oz/200 g) basmati rice

2 cups (17 fl oz/500 ml) chicken stock

¼ tsp saffron threads

½ cup (2¾ oz/80 g) fresh or frozen peas

Peel the shrimp, leaving the tails intact. Gently pull out the dark vein from each shrimp back, starting at the head end. Scrub the mussels with a stiff brush and pull out the hairy beards. Discard any broken mussels, or open ones that don't close when tapped on the bench. Cut the fish fillet into bite-size cubes, checking for bones. Trim the chicken, then cut into bite-size cubes. Score a cross in the base of the tomato. Cover with boiling water for 30 seconds, then plunge into cold water. Drain and peel away the tomato skin from the cross. Chop.

Heat the wine and two-thirds of the onion in a large pan. Add the mussels, cover and gently shake the pan for 4–5 minutes over high heat. After 3 minutes, start removing opened mussels and set aside. At the end of 5 minutes, discard any unopened mussels. Reserve the liquid.

Heat half the oil in a large frying pan. Cook the chicken for 5 minutes, or until golden. Remove from the pan. Add the shrimp, fish and squid and cook for 1 minute. Remove from the pan. Heat the remaining oil and cook the bacon, garlic, pepper and remaining onion for 5 minutes, or until the onion is soft. Add the tomato, sausage and cayenne. Season. Stir in the reserved cooking liquid, then add the rice and mix well.

Bring the stock to a boil in a small saucepan, then reduce to a simmer. Add the saffron, then pour into the rice and mix well. Bring slowly to a boil. Reduce the heat to low and simmer, uncovered, for 15 minutes, without stirring. Push the peas, chicken, shrimp, squid and fish into the rice with a wooden spoon, then cover and cook over low heat for 10–15 minutes, or until the rice is tender and the seafood cooked.

Prep time: 30 minutes

Cooking time: 55 minutes

Serves 4

nutrition per serving Energy 632 Cal (2653 kJ); Fat 23.5 g; Saturated fat 6.1 g; Protein 51 g; Carbohydrate 48.8 g; Fiber 3.1 g; Cholesterol 207 mg

chicken chasseur

This nourishing stew is perfect in cool weather. Make it on the weekend when you have plenty of time to enjoy the succulent aromas while it's cooking.

2 tsp olive or canola oil

2 lb 4 oz (1 kg) boneless, skinless chicken thighs, trimmed

1 garlic clove, crushed

1 large onion, sliced

3½ oz (100 g) button mushrooms, sliced

1 tsp thyme

14 oz (400 g) can tomatoes

3 tbs chicken stock

3 tbs white wine

1 tbs tomato paste

13 oz (375 g) penne

Prep time: 20 minutes
Cooking time: 1½ hours
Serves 4

Preheat the oven to 350°F (180°C/Gas 4). Heat the oil in a heavy-based frying pan and brown the chicken in batches over medium heat. Drain on paper towels, then transfer to a casserole.

Add the garlic, onion and mushrooms to the pan and cook over medium heat for 5 minutes, or until soft. Add to the chicken with the thyme and tomatoes and crush the tomatoes with a wooden spoon.

Combine the stock, wine and tomato paste and pour over the chicken. Cover and bake for 1¼ hours, or until the chicken is tender.

Meanwhile, cook the pasta in a large saucepan of boiling water for 10 minutes, or until *al dente*. Drain well. Serve with the chicken.

nutrition per serving Energy 730 Cal (3066 kJ); Fat 21.7 g; Saturated fat 6 g; Protein 59.9 g; Carbohydrate 71 g; Fiber 6.1 g; Cholesterol 217 mg

tandoori fish cutlets

The tandoori spice mix used in this dish boosts the flavor of the fish and also adds valuable minerals to your diet.

4 fish cutlets
(see Hint)

3 tbs lemon juice

1 onion, finely chopped

2 garlic cloves, crushed

1 tbs grated fresh ginger

1 fresh red chili

1 tbs garam masala

1 tsp paprika

¼ tsp salt

2 cups (1 lb 2 oz/500 g) low-fat plain yogurt

2 cups (14 oz/400 g) basmati rice, rinsed and drained

Prep time: 20 minutes + overnight marinating
Cooking time: 30 minutes
Serves 4

Pat the fish cutlets dry with paper towels and arrange in a shallow non-metallic dish. Drizzle the lemon juice over the fish and turn to coat the cutlets with the juice.

Blend the onion, garlic, ginger, chili, garam masala, paprika and salt in a blender until smooth. Transfer to a bowl and stir in the yogurt. Spoon the marinade over the fish and turn the fish to coat thoroughly. Cover and refrigerate overnight.

Put the rice and 4 cups (35 fl oz/1 liter) water in a saucepan and bring to a boil over medium heat. Reduce the heat to low, cover with a lid and cook for 20 minutes, or until the rice is tender. Remove from the heat and leave to stand, covered, for 5 minutes.

Meanwhile, heat a broiler (grill) or barbecue hotplate. Remove the cutlets from the marinade and allow any excess to drip off. Cook the cutlets under the broiler or on the barbecue for 3–4 minutes on each side, or until the fish flakes easily when tested with a fork. Serve with the rice. Delicious with extra yogurt and baby spinach leaves or cucumber raita.

HINT: Try cod, snapper or kingfish.

nutrition per serving Energy 653 Cal (2743 kJ); Fat 8.2 g; Saturated fat 4.1 g; Protein 53.9 g; Carbohydrate 89 g; Fiber 2.7 g; Cholesterol 142 mg

coq au vin

This recipe contains less fat than the traditional French version of a coq au vin, but still has all the flavor.

2 tsp olive oil

4½ oz (125 g) low-fat bacon (we used 97% fat-free), roughly chopped

3 lb 5 oz (1.5 kg) skinless chicken pieces, trimmed

12 oz (350 g) baby onions

2 tbs all-purpose (plain) flour

3 cups (26 fl oz/750 ml) red wine (see Hint)

9 oz (250 g) field mushrooms, sliced

1 tbs thyme, to garnish

6 wholegrain bread rolls

Prep time: 15 minutes

Cooking time: 1 hour 50 minutes

Serves 6

Preheat the oven to 350°F (180°C/Gas 4). Heat the oil in a large flameproof casserole. Add the bacon and cook until golden, then remove. Add the chicken in batches and cook for 4–5 minutes, or until browned. Remove from the dish. Add the onions and cook for 2–3 minutes, or until browned, then remove from the dish.

Add the flour to the dish and stir well, then remove from the heat and slowly stir in the red wine. Return to the heat, bring to a boil and return the bacon and chicken to the pan. Cover and cook in the oven for 1 hour. Return the onions to the pan and add the mushrooms. Cook for a further 30 minutes. Season to taste with salt and freshly ground black pepper, then garnish with the thyme.

Meanwhile, put the bread rolls in the oven for a few minutes, or until warmed through. Serve with the casserole.

HINT: Burgundy or Pinot Noir would suit the recipe.

nutrition per serving Energy 523 Cal (2198 kJ); Fat 16.6 g; Saturated fat 4.3 g; Protein 41.1 g; Carbohydrate 32.4 g; Fiber 5.2 g; Cholesterol 135 mg

chili con carne
with parsley rice

This popular dish is great for a family meal or casual dinner party. To save time, you can cook the chili ahead of time and store it in the refrigerator for up to 3 days. It also makes delicious leftovers.

2 tsp canola or olive oil

I onion, chopped

3 garlic cloves, crushed

I celery stalk, sliced

I lb 2 oz (500 g) lean ground (minced) beef

2 tsp chili powder

pinch of cayenne pepper

I tbs chopped oregano

14 oz (400 g) can chopped tomatoes

2 tbs tomato paste

1½ cups (10½ oz/300 g) basmati rice, rinsed and drained

4 tbs finely chopped parsley

I tsp soft brown sugar

I tbs cider vinegar or red wine vinegar

14 oz (400 g) can red kidney beans, drained and rinsed

plain yogurt or grated low-fat cheddar cheese, to serve

Prep time: 10 minutes

Cooking time: I hour 5 minutes

Serves 4

Heat the oil in a large, heavy-based saucepan. Add the onion, garlic and celery and stir over medium heat for 5 minutes, or until softened. Add the beef and cook over high heat for 5 minutes, or until well browned. Add the chili powder, cayenne and oregano. Stir well and cook over medium heat for 5 minutes.

Add the tomatoes, tomato paste and ½ cup (4 fl oz/125 ml) water, stir well, then simmer for 30 minutes, stirring occasionally.

Meanwhile, put the rice and 3 cups (26 fl oz/750 ml) water in a saucepan and bring to a boil over medium heat. Reduce the heat to low, cover with a lid and cook for 20 minutes, or until the rice is tender. Remove from the heat and leave to stand, covered, for 5 minutes.

Add the sugar, vinegar and beans to the chili mixture, and season with salt and freshly ground black pepper. Heat through for 5 minutes before serving. Serve with the rice and top with a little plain yogurt or low-fat cheddar cheese, if you like.

nutrition per serving Energy 564 Cal (2370 kJ): Fat 12.3 g; Saturated fat 4.1 g; Protein 36.6 g; Carbohydrate 75.9 g; Fiber 8.3 g; Cholesterol 64 mg

beef in black bean sauce

This popular Chinese dish should give you an energy boost—it's rich in iron, zinc and carbohydrate.

2 garlic cloves, crushed

2 tsp grated fresh ginger

2 tbs dry sherry

1 tbs soy sauce

1 lb 10 oz (750 g) lean beef tip steak

2 cups (14 oz/400 g) basmati rice, rinsed and drained

2 tsp cornstarch (cornflour)

1 tbs canola oil

2 onions, cut into wedges

1 large green pepper (capsicum), cut into strips

8½ oz (235 g) can sliced bamboo shoots, drained and rinsed

2 tbs canned black beans, rinsed, chopped

Prep time: 15 minutes + 1 hour marinating

Cooking time: 30 minutes

Serves 4

To make the marinade, combine the garlic, ginger, sherry and soy sauce in a non-metallic bowl. Trim the meat, then slice across the grain into long, thin strips. Add to the marinade and toss to coat well. Cover with plastic wrap and refrigerate for at least 1 hour, turning occasionally. Drain the meat, reserving the marinade.

Put the rice and 4 cups (35 fl oz/1 liter) water in a saucepan and bring to a boil over medium heat. Reduce the heat to low, cover with a lid and cook for 20 minutes, or until the rice is tender. Remove from the heat and leave to stand, covered, for 5 minutes.

Meanwhile, to make the stir-fry sauce, mix the cornstarch and remaining marinade with 2 tablespoons water until smooth.

Heat a wok until very hot, add half of the oil and swirl to coat. Add the meat in small batches and stir-fry briefly until browned but not cooked through. Remove from the wok and drain on paper towels. Reheat the wok between batches.

Heat the remaining oil in the wok and swirl to coat. Add the onion and pepper and stir-fry over high heat for 3 minutes, or until the onion is soft. Add the bamboo shoots and black beans, then cook for 1 minute. Return the meat to the wok along with the stir-fry sauce and stir-fry over high heat until the meat is cooked through and the sauce has thickened. Serve immediately with the rice.

HINT: Left-over black beans can be refrigerated for up to 2 weeks.

nutrition per serving Energy 688 Cal (2890 kJ); Fat 14.2 g; Saturated fat 4.8 g; Protein 49.7 g; Carbohydrate 87.4 g; Fiber 3.1 g; Cholesterol 121 mg

greek-style calamari

This dish has less fat and more nutrients than deep-fried calamari. Serve with salad and wholegrain bread for a complete meal.

STUFFING

2 tsp olive oil

2 scallions (spring onions), chopped

1½ cups (10 oz/280 g) cold, cooked basmati rice (see *Hint*)

⅓ cup (2¼ oz/60 g) pine nuts

⅓ cup (2¼ oz/60 g) dried apricots, finely chopped

2 tbs chopped parsley

2 tsp finely grated lemon zest

1 egg, lightly beaten

2 lb 4 oz (1 kg) squid hoods

SAUCE

4 large ripe tomatoes

2 tsp olive oil

1 onion, finely chopped

1 garlic clove, crushed

3 tbs good-quality red wine

1 tbs chopped oregano

Prep time: 30 minutes
Cooking time: 35 minutes
Serves 4–6

Preheat the oven to 315°F (160°C/Gas 2–3).

To make the stuffing, mix the oil, scallions, rice, pine nuts, apricots, parsley and lemon zest in a bowl. Add enough egg to moisten all the ingredients.

Wash the squid hoods and pat dry inside and out with paper towels. Three-quarters fill each hood with the stuffing. Secure the ends with toothpicks or skewers. Place in a single layer in a casserole.

To make the sauce, begin by peeling the tomatoes. Score a cross in the base of each one. Cover with boiling water for 30 seconds, then plunge into cold water. Drain and peel away the tomato skin from the cross. Chop the flesh. Heat the oil in a frying pan. Add the onion and garlic and cook over low heat for 2 minutes, or until the onion is soft. Add the tomato, wine and oregano and bring to a boil. Reduce the heat, cover and cook over low heat for 10 minutes.

Pour the hot sauce over the squid, cover and bake for 20 minutes, or until the squid is tender. Remove the toothpicks before cutting into thick slices for serving. Spoon the sauce over just before serving.

HINT: You will need to cook ½ cup (3½ oz/100 g) basmati rice for this recipe.

nutrition per serving (6) Energy 346 Cal (1454 kJ); Fat 13.2 g; Saturated fat 1.8 g; Protein 33.4 g; Carbohydrate 21.7 g; Fiber 3.9 g; Cholesterol 363 mg

osso bucco with gremolata

A great winter warmer, osso bucco can be served with pasta or grainy bread. It is even more delicious when served the next day as the flavors intensify.

GREMOLATA

1 tbs finely shredded lemon zest

1–2 garlic cloves, finely chopped

3 tbs finely chopped parsley

all-purpose (plain) flour, for dusting

4 veal shank pieces, each 2 in (5 cm) thick

2 tsp olive oil

2 large onions, sliced

6 plum (Roma) tomatoes, finely chopped

2 tbs tomato paste

1½ cups (13 fl oz/375 ml) white wine

1 tbs cornstarch (cornflour)

2–3 garlic cloves, crushed

1 small bunch (about 2¼ oz/ 60 g) parsley, finely chopped

13 oz (375 g) penne

Prep time: 40 minutes

Cooking time: 2½ hours

Serves 4

To make the gremolata, mix together the lemon zest, garlic and parsley and set aside.

Season the flour with salt and freshly ground black pepper. Toss the veal pieces in the flour, shaking off any excess. Heat half the oil in a heavy-based frying pan large enough to fit the meat in a single layer. When the oil is hot, brown the veal on both sides. Remove and set aside.

Heat the remaining oil in the pan and cook the onion for 2–3 minutes, or until soft but not brown. Add the meat in a single layer so that it fits snugly in the pan. Season with salt and freshly ground black pepper.

Mix together the tomatoes, tomato paste and wine and pour the mixture over the meat. Bring to a boil, then reduce the heat, cover and simmer for 1½ hours.

Remove 1 cup (9 fl oz/250 ml) of the cooking liquid and set aside to cool slightly. Put the cornstarch in a small bowl and whisk in the reserved liquid, then stir in the garlic and chopped parsley and add the mixture to the pan. Simmer, uncovered, for about 30 minutes, or until the meat is very tender and the sauce has thickened. Sprinkle with the gremolata just before serving.

Meanwhile, cook the pasta in a large saucepan of boiling water for 10 minutes, or until *al dente*. Drain well. Serve with the veal. Delicious with a green salad.

nutrition per serving Energy 582 Cal (2446 kJ); Fat 6.2 g; Saturated fat 1.3 g; Protein 36.9 g; Carbohydrate 78.1 g; Fiber 7.6 g; Cholesterol 86 mg

rosemary lamb with cannellini beans

This meal will satisfy the heartiest of appetites—it provides
plenty of protein, fiber and low-GI starch.

1 lb 5 oz (600 g) lean lamb
tenderloin (fillet)

2 tomatoes

13 oz (375 g) small shell pasta

canola or olive oil spray

3 garlic cloves, finely chopped

1 tsp cumin seeds

2 tsp finely chopped rosemary

2 tbs red wine vinegar

1 tbs lemon juice

10½ oz (300 g) can cannellini
beans, drained and rinsed

2 tbs chopped Italian
(flat-leaf) parsley

Prep time: 20 minutes
Cooking time: 20 minutes
Serves 4

Trim the lamb, then slice on the diagonal. To peel the tomatoes,
score a cross in the base of each one. Cover with boiling water for
30 seconds, then plunge into cold water. Drain and peel away the skin
from the cross. Scoop out the seeds with a teaspoon and finely chop
the flesh into cubes.

Cook the pasta in a large saucepan of boiling water for 10 minutes, or
until *al dente*. Drain well.

Meanwhile, heat a large frying pan until very hot and spray with the
oil. Add the lamb in two batches and cook over very high heat, stirring
frequently until it is browned.

Return all the lamb to the pan, then add the garlic, cumin and
rosemary. Cook for 1 minute. Reduce the heat and pour in the
vinegar and lemon juice. Stir to combine, scraping any sediment from
the bottom of the pan.

Add the tomato and cannellini beans and stir-fry until warmed
through. Season with salt and freshly ground black pepper, then
sprinkle with the parsley. Serve with the pasta.

nutrition per serving Energy 546 Cal (2291 kJ);
Fat 7.5 g; Saturated fat 2.7 g; Protein 46.2 g;
Carbohydrate 72.5 g; Fiber 7.9 g; Cholesterol 97 mg

lasagna

A perennial favourite, this version has all the flavor but less fat than traditional lasagne, but is just as hard to resist.

2 tsp olive oil

I large onion, chopped

2 carrots, finely chopped

2 celery stalks, finely chopped

2 zucchini (courgettes), finely chopped

2 garlic cloves, crushed

I lb 2 oz (500 g) lean ground (minced) beef

2 x 14 oz (400 g) cans chopped tomatoes

½ cup (4 fl oz/125 ml) beef stock

2 tbs tomato paste

2 tsp dried oregano

13 oz (375 g) instant lasagna sheets

CHEESE SAUCE

3 cups (26 fl oz/750 ml) skim or non-fat milk

⅓ cup (1½ oz/40 g) cornstarch (cornflour)

3½ oz (100 g) reduced-fat cheddar cheese

Prep time: 40 minutes

Cooking time: I hour 35 minutes

Serves 8

Heat the oil in a large non-stick saucepan over medium heat. Add the onion and cook for 5 minutes, or until soft. Add the carrot, celery and zucchini and cook, stirring constantly, for 5 minutes, or until soft. Add the garlic and cook for one minute. Increase the heat to high, add the beef and cook, stirring, until well browned. Break up any lumps with a wooden spoon. Add the tomato, stock, tomato paste and oregano to the pan and stir well. Bring to a boil, then reduce the heat and simmer gently, partially covered, for 20 minutes, stirring occasionally to prevent the mixture sticking to the pan.

Preheat the oven to 350°F (180°C/Gas 4). Spread a little of the meat sauce into the base of a 9 x 12 in (23 x 30 cm) ovenproof dish. Arrange a layer of lasagna sheets in the dish, breaking some of the sheets, if necessary, to fit in neatly. Spread half the meat sauce over the top to cover evenly. Cover with another layer of lasagna sheets, a layer of meat sauce, then a final layer of lasagna sheets.

To make the cheese sauce, blend a little of the milk with the cornstarch, to form a smooth paste, in a small saucepan. Gradually blend in the remaining milk and stir constantly over low heat until the mixture boils and thickens. Remove from the heat and stir in the cheese until melted.

Spread the sauce evenly over the top of the lasagna. Bake for I hour, checking after 25 minutes. If the top is browning too quickly, cover loosely with non-stick baking paper or foil sprayed with oil. Take care when removing the paper or foil that the topping does not lift off.

nutrition per serving Energy 384 Cal (1612 kJ); Fat 9 g; Saturated fat 3.8 g; Protein 27.3 g; Carbohydrate 49.2 g; Fiber 4.6 g; Cholesterol 43 mg

japanese-style salmon wraps

Cooking the salmon together with vegetables and spices makes the fish tender and full of flavor—a delicious way to eat fish.

1 cup (7 oz/200 g) basmati rice, rinsed and drained

10½ oz (300 g) can chickpeas, drained

2 tsp sesame seeds

4 x 5½ oz (150 g) salmon cutlets or fillets

1 in (2.5 cm) piece fresh ginger

2 celery stalks

4 scallions (spring onions)

¼ tsp dashi granules

3 tbs mirin rice wine

2 tbs tamari

Prep time: 40 minutes
Cooking time: 35 minutes
Serves 4

Put the rice and 1½ cups (13 fl oz/375 ml) water in a saucepan and bring to a boil over medium heat. Reduce the heat to low, cover with a lid and cook for 20 minutes, or until the rice is tender. Remove from the heat and leave to stand, covered, for 5 minutes. Stir the chickpeas through the rice.

Meanwhile, cut out four squares of baking paper large enough to enclose the salmon steaks. Preheat the oven to 450°F (230°C/Gas 8).

Dry-fry the sesame seeds over low heat in a small frying pan, then remove from the pan.

Wash the salmon and pat dry with paper towels. Put a salmon cutlet in the center of each paper square.

Cut the ginger into paper-thin slices. Slice the celery and scallions into long thin strips. Arrange a bundle of the prepared strips and several slices of ginger on each salmon steak.

Combine the dashi granules, mirin and tamari in a small saucepan. Stir gently over low heat until the granules dissolve. Drizzle over each bundle, sprinkle with sesame seeds and carefully wrap the salmon, folding in the sides to seal in all the juices. Arrange the parcels in a bamboo steamer over a large saucepan of simmering water and steam for about 15 minutes. (The paper will puff up when the fish is cooked.) Serve immediately with the rice and chickpeas.

nutrition per serving Energy 470 Cal (1976 kJ); Fat 12.7 g; Saturated fat 2.7 g; Protein 38.2 g; Carbohydrate 49.4 g; Fiber 4.8 g; Cholesterol 78 mg

beef and shiitake mushroom stir-fry

This recipe is good to add to your collection of favorite weekday recipes. It delivers good amounts of protein, B vitamins, iron and zinc.

6 dried shiitake mushrooms

I tbs teriyaki marinade

4 garlic cloves, finely chopped

I red chili, finely chopped

14 oz (400 g) lean top loin steak

10½ oz (300 g) mung bean noodles

canola oil spray

I tsp canola oil

2 onions, very thinly sliced

4 scallions (spring onions), chopped

½ red pepper (capsicum), thinly sliced

½ cup (4 fl oz/125 ml) ready-made puréed tomatoes

I tsp soft brown sugar

2 tomatoes, diced

I tsp sesame oil

2 tbs shredded basil

Prep time: 25 minutes + 20 minutes soaking + 20 minutes marinating

Cooking time: 15 minutes

Serves 4

Put the mushrooms in a bowl, cover with boiling water and soak for 20 minutes. Drain, squeeze dry and thinly slice, discarding the stalks.

To make the marinade, combine the ready-made teriyaki marinade, garlic, chili and some salt and freshly ground black pepper in a large non-metallic bowl. Trim the steak, then cut into thin strips. Add to the marinade and toss well. Marinate for at least 20 minutes.

Put the noodles in a bowl and cover with warm water. Soak for 10 minutes, or until translucent. Put the noodles in a saucepan of boiling water and cook for 15 minutes, or until tender. Rinse under cold water, then drain. Use scissors to cut into shorter lengths.

Heat a wok until very hot and spray with the oil. Add the steak in two batches. Stir-fry over high heat for 30 seconds, or until just browned. Remove all the meat from the wok and set aside. Reheat the wok between batches.

Reheat the wok, add the oil and stir-fry the onion, scallion and pepper for 3 minutes, or until golden. Add the mushrooms, puréed tomatoes and sugar. Bring to a boil, then reduce the heat and simmer for 3 minutes. Return the beef to the wok along with the noodles, diced tomato and sesame oil and season with salt and freshly ground black pepper. Bring to a boil, allowing the tomato to heat through. Stir in the basil. Serve immediately.

nutrition per serving Energy 485 Cal (2030 kJ); Fat 7.3 g; Saturated fat 2.1 g; Protein 24.8 g; Carbohydrate 76.8 g; Fiber 4.4 g; Cholesterol 57 mg

greek-style lamb

Delicious, nutritious and ready in a flash—what more could you want!

14 oz (400 g) lean lamb tenderloins (fillets)

olive oil spray

1 tsp olive oil

1 large red onion, sliced

3 zucchini (courgettes), thinly sliced

7 oz (200 g) cherry tomatoes, halved

3 garlic cloves, crushed

½ cup (2¼ oz/60 g) pitted black olives in brine, drained and cut in half

2 tbs lemon juice

2 tbs finely chopped oregano

3½ oz (100 g) low-fat feta cheese, crumbled

⅓ cup (1¾ oz/50 g) pine nuts, lightly toasted

4 wholegrain bread rolls or stoneground whole wheat (wholemeal) pita bread pockets, warmed

Prep time: 20 minutes

Cooking time: 10 minutes

Serves 4

Trim the lamb, then cut across the grain into thin strips. Heat a large frying pan until hot and spray with the oil. Add the lamb in small batches and cook each batch over high heat for 1–2 minutes, or until browned. Remove all the lamb from the pan.

Heat the oil in the pan, then add the onion and zucchini. Cook, stirring, over high heat for 2 minutes, or until just tender. Add the cherry tomatoes and garlic. Cook for 1–2 minutes, or until the tomatoes have just softened. Return the meat to the pan and stir over high heat until heated through.

Remove the pan from the heat. Add the olives, lemon juice and oregano and toss until well combined. Sprinkle with crumbled feta cheese and pine nuts before serving. Serve with the bread rolls or pockets and a mixed green salad.

nutrition per serving Energy 451 Cal (1892 kJ); Fat 20 g; Saturated fat 5.5 g; Protein 34.6 g; Carbohydrate 31.1 g; Fiber 7.2 g; Cholesterol 78 mg

thai chicken and basil stir-fry

This aromatic Thai meal provides good amounts of most vitamins and minerals. The fresh flavors are perfect to enjoy on a summer night.

14 oz (400 g) fresh rice noodles

3 tbs fish sauce

3 tbs lime juice

1 tomato, diced

2 handfuls Thai basil

1 lb 2 oz (500 g) boneless, skinless chicken breasts

2 tsp canola oil

3 garlic cloves, thinly sliced

4 scallions (spring onions), thinly sliced

2 small red chilies, seeded and thinly sliced

9 oz (250 g) snow peas (mangetout), trimmed

Prep time: 15 minutes
Cooking time: 20 minutes
Serves 4

Put the rice noodles in a large heatproof bowl, cover with boiling water and soak for 8 minutes, or until softened. Separate gently and drain. Use scissors to cut into shorter lengths.

Meanwhile, to make the stir-fry sauce, put the fish sauce, lime juice, tomato, basil and 1 tablespoon water in a small bowl and mix well.

Trim the chicken and thinly slice. Heat a wok over high heat, add the oil and swirl to coat. Add the garlic, scallion and chili and stir-fry for 1 minute, or until fragrant. Add the chicken in small batches and stir-fry for 3 minutes, or until lightly browned. Remove from the wok and set aside. Reheat the wok between batches.

Return all the chicken to the wok. Add the snow peas and stir-fry sauce to the wok and scrape any sediment from the bottom. Stir through the noodles. Reduce the heat and simmer for 2 minutes, or until the tomato is soft and the chicken cooked through. Serve immediately.

nutrition per serving Energy 432 Cal (1807 kJ); Fat 10.3 g; Saturated fat 2.3 g; Protein 34.8 g; Carbohydrate 46.7 g; Fiber 4.1 g; Cholesterol 82 mg

peppered lamb and asparagus stir-fry

Mung bean vermicelli is rich in low-GI starch. Together with the beef and vegetables, this makes a very filling meal.

10½ oz (300 g) dried mung bean vermicelli

2 tsp green peppercorns, finely chopped

3 garlic cloves, finely chopped

1 tbs canola oil

14 oz (400 g) lean lamb tenderloins (fillets)

canola oil spray

1 onion, cut into small wedges

4 tbs dry sherry

1 green pepper (capsicum), cut into strips

16 small asparagus spears, trimmed and cut into bite-size pieces

7 oz (200 g) broccoli florets

2 tbs oyster sauce

garlic chives, cut into short lengths, to garnish

Prep time: 35 minutes +
20 minutes marinating +
10 minutes soaking

Cooking time: 30 minutes

Serves 4

Put the noodles in a large bowl and cover with warm water. Soak for 10 minutes, or until they are translucent. Transfer to a saucepan of boiling water and cook for 15 minutes, or until tender. Rinse under cold water, then drain. Use scissors to cut into shorter lengths.

To make the marinade, put the green peppercorns, garlic and oil in a large non-metallic bowl. Add the lamb and toss well to coat. Cover with plastic wrap and marinate for 20 minutes.

Trim the lamb and cut into bite-size pieces. Heat a wok over high heat until slightly smoking. Add the lamb in small batches and stir-fry briefly until browned and just cooked. Remove from the wok and keep warm. Reheat the wok between batches.

Reheat the wok, spray with oil and stir-fry the onion and 2 teaspoons of the sherry for 1 minute. Add the pepper and a large pinch of salt. Cover, steam for 2 minutes, add the asparagus, broccoli and the remaining sherry and stir-fry for 1 minute. Cover and steam for 3 minutes, or until the vegetables are just tender. Return the lamb to the pan, add the oyster sauce and stir to combine with the vegetables. Add the noodles and stir through until warmed. Serve garnished with the chives.

nutrition per serving Energy 486 Cal (2041 kJ); Fat 8.7 g; Saturated fat 2 g; Protein 25.5 g; Carbohydrate 70.3 g; Fiber 4.3 g; Cholesterol 65 mg

beef bourguignon

This dish is a French classic—a hearty stew that is both flavoursome and satisfying, and makes delicious leftovers.

2 lb 4 oz (1 kg) lean top loin or round steak

all-purpose (plain) flour, for dusting

1¾ oz (50 g) low-fat bacon (we used 97% fat-free)

2 tsp olive or canola oil

12 baby onions

1 cup (9 fl oz/250 ml) red wine

2 cups (17 fl oz/500 ml) beef stock

1 tsp dried thyme

7 oz (200 g) button mushrooms

2 bay leaves

13 oz (375 g) fettuccine

Prep time: 20 minutes

Cooking time: 2 hours

Serves 6

Trim the steak and cut into ¾ in (2 cm) cubes. Season the flour with salt and freshly ground black pepper. Lightly toss the steak in the flour, shaking off the excess.

Cut the bacon into ¾ in (2 cm) squares. Heat the oil in a large heavy-based saucepan and briefly cook the bacon over medium heat. Remove the bacon from the pan, then add the meat and brown well in batches. Remove and set aside. Add the onions to the pan and cook until golden.

Return the bacon and meat to the pan with the remaining ingredients. Bring to a boil, reduce the heat and simmer, covered, for 1½ hours, or until the meat is very tender, stirring occasionally. Remove the bay leaves to serve.

Meanwhile, cook the pasta in a large saucepan of boiling water for 10 minutes, or until *al dente*. Drain well. Serve with the beef. Delicious with a green salad or steamed mixed vegetables.

HINT: Will keep refrigerated in an airtight container for up to 3 days.

nutrition per serving Energy 510 Cal (2143 kJ); Fat 9.7 g; Saturated fat 3.4 g; Protein 48.4 g; Carbohydrate 50 g; Fiber 3.3 g; Cholesterol 106 mg

beef stroganoff

This recipe contains less fat than the regular version, but is still rich in flavor. Using evaporated milk instead of cream cuts lots of fat and calories while still producing a delicious creamy sauce.

1 lb 2 oz (500 g) lean beef tip steak

canola or olive oil spray

1 onion, sliced

¼ tsp paprika

9 oz (250 g) button mushrooms, halved

2 tbs tomato paste

½ cup (4 fl oz/125 ml) beef stock

13 oz (375 g) fettuccine

½ cup (4 fl oz/125 ml) low-fat evaporated milk

3 tsp cornstarch (cornflour)

3 tbs chopped parsley

Prep time: 20 minutes
Cooking time: 30 minutes
Serves 4

Trim the steak and slice into thin strips. Heat a large non-stick frying pan over high heat. Spray with the oil. Add the steak in batches and cook for 2–3 minutes, or until just cooked. Remove from the pan.

Lightly spray the pan with oil and cook the onion, paprika and mushrooms over medium heat until the onion has softened. Add the meat, tomato paste, stock and ½ cup (4 fl oz/125 ml) water. Bring to a boil, then reduce the heat and simmer for 10 minutes.

Meanwhile, cook the pasta in a large saucepan of boiling water for 10 minutes, or until *al dente*. Drain well.

In a small bowl, mix the evaporated milk with the cornstarch. Add to the beef pan and stir until the sauce boils and thickens. Sprinkle with parsley and serve with the fettuccine.

nutrition per serving Energy 562 Cal (2362 kJ): Fat 8.7 g; Saturated fat 3 g; Protein 45.2 g; Carbohydrate 74.7 g; Fiber 5 g; Cholesterol 99 mg

chicken and tomato curry

This spicy dish will satisfy curry lovers.

2 x 3 lb 5 oz (1.5 kg) chickens
canola or olive oil spray
1 tbs canola or olive oil
1 onion, sliced
½ tsp ground cloves
1 tsp ground turmeric
2 tsp garam masala
3 tsp chili powder
3 garlic cloves, peeled
1 tbs finely chopped fresh ginger
1 tbs poppy seeds
2 tsp fennel seeds
3 cardamom pods, seeds removed
1 cup (9 fl oz/250 ml) light coconut milk
1 star anise
1 cinnamon stick
4 large tomatoes, chopped
2 tbs lime juice
2 cups (14 oz/400 g) basmati rice, rinsed and drained
1 cup (9 oz/250 g) low-fat plain yogurt

Prep time: 35 minutes
Cooking time: 2 hours
Serves 10

Remove the skin from the chickens, cut into pieces, then trim off the fat.

Heat 2 teaspoons of the oil in a large frying pan over medium heat, then add the chicken in batches and cook for 5–10 minutes, or until browned, then transfer to a large saucepan.

Heat the remaining oil and add the onion to the frying pan and cook over medium heat, stirring, for 10–12 minutes, or until golden. Stir in the ground cloves, turmeric, garam masala and chili powder, and cook, stirring, for 1 minute, then transfer to the pan with the chicken.

Put the garlic, ginger and poppy, fennel and cardamom seeds and 2 tablespoons of the coconut milk in a food processor or blender, and process until smooth.

Add the spice mixture, remaining coconut milk, star anise, cinnamon, tomato and 3 tablespoons water to the pan with the chicken. Simmer, covered, for 45 minutes, or until the chicken is tender. Remove the chicken, cover and keep warm. Bring the cooking liquid to a boil and boil for 20–25 minutes, or until reduced by half. Mix the lime juice with the cooking liquid and pour over the chicken.

Meanwhile, put the rice and 4 cups (35 fl oz/1 liter) water in a saucepan and bring to a boil over medium heat. Reduce the heat to low, cover with a lid and cook for 20 minutes, or until the rice is tender. Remove from the heat and leave to stand, covered, for 5 minutes. Serve with the chicken and yogurt.

nutrition per serving Energy 419 Cal (1761 kJ); Fat 15.7 g; Saturated fat 5 g; Protein 32.4 g; Carbohydrate 36.9 g; Fiber 2.7 g; Cholesterol 126 mg

middle-eastern
chicken with bulghur wheat

A nourishing meal that tastes great and is easy to make. This is a good way to include low-GI bulghur wheat and chickpeas in your diet.

2 cups (12 oz/350 g) bulghur wheat (burghul)

2 boneless, skinless chicken breasts

2 tsp olive oil

1 red onion, thinly sliced

10½ oz (300 g) can chickpeas, drained and rinsed

½ cup (2½ oz/70 g) unsalted pistachio kernels

1 tomato, chopped

juice of 1 orange

4 tbs finely chopped Italian (flat-leaf) parsley

Prep time: 15 minutes + 15 minutes soaking

Cooking time: 20 minutes

Serves 4

Put the bulghur wheat in a bowl, cover with water and leave to soak for 15 minutes, or until the bulghur wheat has softened. Drain and use clean hands to squeeze dry.

Meanwhile, trim the chicken and thinly slice. Heat a large frying pan over high heat, add half the oil and swirl to coat. Add the chicken in batches and stir-fry for 3–5 minutes, or until cooked. Remove from the pan and keep warm. Reheat the pan between batches.

Add the remaining oil to the pan and cook the onion, stirring, for 2 minutes, then add the chickpeas, pistachio kernels and tomato. Cook, stirring, for 3–5 minutes, or until the chickpeas are warmed through.

Pour in the orange juice, return the chicken and its juices to the pan and cook until half the juice has evaporated. Stir in the parsley. Season well with salt and freshly ground black pepper and serve with the bulghur wheat.

nutrition per serving Energy 592 Cal (2485 kJ); Fat 18.9 g; Saturated fat 3.2 g; Protein 39.6 g; Carbohydrate 63.3 g; Fiber 20.9 g; Cholesterol 66 mg

meatloaf

Preparing a family dinner doesn't have to be hard work. Meatloaf is a great way to get children to eat vegetables—simply grate them and add them to the mixture.

2¼ oz (60 g) sweet potato, peeled

1 carrot

canola or olive oil spray

2 onions, finely chopped

2 garlic cloves, crushed

1½ cups (4½ oz/125 g) fresh wholegrain breadcrumbs

2 tbs chopped parsley

1 lb 2 oz (500 g) lean ground (minced) beef

2 tbs worcestershire sauce

1 tsp dried basil

1 tbs tomato paste

10½ oz (300 g) can chickpeas, drained and rinsed

1 egg, lightly beaten

1 cup (3¼ oz/90 g) button mushrooms, thinly sliced

14 oz (400 g) can tomatoes

1 tbs dry white wine

1 tsp soft brown sugar

Prep time: 20 minutes

Cooking time: 1 hour 20 minutes

Serves 6

Preheat the oven to 400°F (200°C/Gas 6). Coarsely grate the sweet potato and carrot.

Heat a non-stick frying pan over medium heat, then spray with the oil. Add the onion and cook, stirring, for 2 minutes. Add 1 tablespoon water to prevent sticking, then add the garlic and stir for 3 minutes, or until the onion is golden brown. Set aside to cool completely.

Use your hands to thoroughly mix together the breadcrumbs, parsley, beef, worcestershire sauce, basil, tomato paste, grated sweet potato and carrot and the cooled onion mixture. Mix in the chickpeas, egg and mushrooms. Season with salt and freshly ground black pepper. Transfer to a 4 × 7 in (10 × 18 cm) non-stick loaf pan (or loaf pan lined with greaseproof paper), pressing gently into the pan and smoothing the top.

To make the tomato sauce, push the undrained tomatoes through a sieve, then discard the contents of the sieve. Add the wine and sugar to the tomato mixture, then stir well. Spoon 3 tablespoons of the sauce over the meatloaf and bake for 15 minutes. Spoon another 3 tablespoons of sauce over the meatloaf, reduce the oven temperature to 375°F (190°C/Gas 5) and bake for 1 hour 10 minutes, basting occasionally with sauce. Slice and serve with any remaining sauce. Delicious with a green salad and wholegrain bread.

nutrition per serving Energy 272 Cal (1138 kJ); Fat 8.6 g; Saturated fat 2.9 g; Protein 24 g; Carbohydrate 21.6 g; Fiber 5 g; Cholesterol 74 mg

spaghetti bolognese

This meaty sauce goes well with most types of pasta, so you can swap the spaghetti with other types of pasta for a new twist.

olive oil spray
2 onions, finely chopped
2 garlic cloves, finely chopped
2 carrots, finely chopped
2 celery stalks, finely chopped
14 oz (400 g) lean ground (minced) beef
2 lb 4 oz (1 kg) tomatoes, chopped
½ cup (4 fl oz/125 ml) red wine
12 oz (350 g) spaghetti
3 tbs finely chopped parsley

Prep time: 20 minutes
Cooking time: 1 hour 20 minutes
Serves 6

Heat a large saucepan over medium heat. Spray with the oil, then add the onion, garlic, carrot and celery. Stir for 5 minutes, or until the vegetables have softened. Add 1 tablespoon water, if necessary, to prevent sticking.

Increase the heat to high, add the beef and cook for 5 minutes, or until browned. Stir constantly to prevent the meat sticking. Add the tomatoes, wine and 1 cup (9 fl oz/250 ml) water. Bring to a boil, reduce the heat and simmer, uncovered, for about 1 hour, until the sauce has thickened.

Meanwhile, cook the spaghetti in a large saucepan of boiling water for 10 minutes, or until *al dente*. Drain. Stir the parsley through the sauce, season with salt and freshly ground black pepper and serve over the pasta. Delicious with a salad and vinegar-based dressing.

HINT: This dish tastes even better the next day and can be kept in the refrigerator for up to 2 days or frozen for up to 1 month.

nutrition per serving Energy 341 Cal (1431 kJ); Fat 6.2 g; Saturated fat 2.1 g; Protein 23 g; Carbohydrate 44.1 g; Fiber 7.4 g; Cholesterol 34 mg

slow-cooked lamb shanks with barley

This is a perfect meal for cold winter weekends. The lamb shanks in this hearty dish are slowly cooked until they are tender. The fiber-rich barley will keep you going for hours.

2 tsp canola oil

4 lean lamb shanks

2 red onions, sliced

10 garlic cloves, peeled

14 oz (400 g) can chopped tomatoes

½ cup (4 fl oz/125 ml) dry white wine

1 bay leaf

1 tsp grated lemon zest

1 large red pepper (capsicum), chopped

1½ cups (11½ oz/325 g) pearl barley

3 tbs chopped parsley

Prep time: 20 minutes

Cooking time: 3¼ hours

Serves 4

Preheat the oven to 325°F (170°C/Gas 3). Heat the oil in a large flameproof casserole, add the shanks in batches and cook over high heat until browned on all sides. Remove the lamb to a side plate.

Add the onion and garlic to the dish and cook until softened. Return all the lamb to the casserole. Add the tomato, wine, bay leaf, lemon zest, pepper and ½ cup (4 fl oz/125 ml) water and bring to a boil. Cover the dish and cook in the oven for 2–2½ hours, or until the meat is tender and falling off the bone and the sauce has thickened.

Meanwhile, wash the barley, then drain well. Put it in a large saucepan with 5 cups (44 fl oz/1.25 liters) water. Bring to a boil, then simmer for 30 minutes, or until soft. Drain.

Season the shanks with salt and freshly ground black pepper to taste. Sprinkle the parsley over the top before serving. Serve with the barley and a salad.

If you find barley difficult to eat at first, try adding cooked barley to cooked basmati rice in progressively larger amounts, so you become used to the flavor and texture. The more barley you add, the lower the GI of the barley rice mix.

nutrition per serving Energy 520 Cal (2184 kJ); Fat 15.1 g; Saturated fat 5.3 g; Protein 33 g; Carbohydrate 57.8 g; Fiber 12.9 g; Cholesterol 75 mg

chicken with snow peas, sprouts and vermicelli noodles

A quick and easy recipe that gives you a complete meal in one dish.

10½ oz (300 g) dried mung bean vermicelli

1 lb 2 oz (500 g) boneless, skinless chicken breasts

2 tsp canola oil

1 onion, thinly sliced

3 kaffir lime leaves, shredded

1 red pepper (capsicum), sliced

2½ oz (75 g) snow peas (mangetout), trimmed

3 tbs lime juice

3½ fl oz (100 ml) soy sauce

1¾ oz (50 g) snow pea (mangetout) sprouts, trimmed

2 tbs chopped cilantro (coriander) leaves

Prep time: 15 minutes + 10 minutes soaking

Cooking time: 30 minutes

Serves 4

Put the noodles in a large bowl and cover with warm water. Soak for 10 minutes, or until they are translucent. Drain. Transfer to a saucepan of boiling water and cook for 10 minutes, or until tender. Rinse under cold water and drain.

Meanwhile, trim the chicken and cut into thin slices. Heat a wok over medium heat, add the oil and swirl to coat. Add the onion and kaffir lime leaves and stir-fry for 3–5 minutes, or until the onion begins to soften. Remove from the wok. Add the chicken in batches and cook for a further 4 minutes, or until lightly browned. Remove from the wok and set aside. Reheat the wok between batches.

Return the onion mixture and all the chicken to the wok, add the pepper and snow peas and continue to cook for 2–3 minutes. Stir in the lime juice and soy sauce and 2 tablespoons of water and cook for 1–2 minutes, or until the sauce reduces slightly. Add the noodles and toss through the mixture to warm through. Add the sprouts and cilantro and cook until the sprouts have wilted slightly.

HINT: Use the chicken, soy sauce and lime juice as a base, and add vegetables and herbs to your taste. For example, try fresh asparagus, or mint and basil instead of cilantro (coriander).

nutrition per serving Energy 505 Cal (2116 kJ); Fat 9.3 g; Saturated fat 2.3 g; Protein 30.9 g; Carbohydrate 71.3 g; Fiber 2.1 g; Cholesterol 82 mg

tuna kabobs with chickpea tomato salsa

Many people lack enough healthy omega-3 fats in their diet. Tuna is a good way to increase these fats, plus zinc.

2 tsp olive oil

2–3 small red chilies, seeded and finely chopped

3–4 garlic cloves, crushed

1 red onion, finely chopped

3 tomatoes, seeded and chopped

3 tbs white wine or water

2 x 10½ oz (300 g) cans chickpeas, drained and rinsed

3 tbs chopped oregano

4 tbs chopped parsley

2 lb 4 oz (1 kg) tuna fillet

olive oil spray

lemon wedges, to serve

Prep time: 20 minutes

Cooking time: 20 minutes

Serves 4

To make the salsa, heat the oil in a large saucepan, add the chili, garlic and onion and stir for 5 minutes, or until softened. Add the tomato and wine. Cook over low heat for 10 minutes, or until the mixture is soft, pulpy and the liquid has evaporated. Stir in the chickpeas, oregano and parsley. Season with salt and freshly ground black pepper.

Meanwhile, trim the tuna and cut into 1½ in (4 cm) cubes. Heat a charbroil pan or barbecue hotplate. Thread the tuna onto 8 metal skewers, lightly spray with the oil, then cook, turning, for 3 minutes. Do not overcook or the tuna will fall apart. Serve with the salsa and lemon wedges.

HINT: Also delicious served with tabbouleh (see recipe on page 72).

nutrition per serving Energy 534 Cal (2244 kJ); Fat 20 g; Saturated fat 6.6 g; Protein 70.6 g; Carbohydrate 17 g; Fiber 7.7 g; Cholesterol 90 mg

chicken with baked eggplant and tomato

A colorful Mediterranean-style meal that provides good amounts of protein, antioxidants, folate and minerals.

1 red pepper (capsicum)

1 eggplant (aubergine)

3 tomatoes

7 oz (200 g) large button mushrooms

1 onion

canola or olive oil spray

1½ tbs tomato paste

½ cup (4 fl oz/125 ml) chicken stock

3 tbs dry white wine

2 slices low-fat bacon (we used 97% fat-free)

4 boneless, skinless chicken breasts

4 small sprigs rosemary

Prep time: 30 minutes

Cooking time: 1½ hours

Serves 4

Preheat the oven to 400°F (200°C/Gas 6). Cut the pepper and eggplant into bite-size pieces. Cut the tomatoes into quarters, the mushrooms in half and the onion into thin wedges. Mix the vegetables together in a roasting pan. Spray with the oil and bake for 1 hour, or until starting to brown and soften, stirring once.

Mix together the tomato paste, stock and wine, then pour into the roasting pan and roast for 10 minutes, or until thickened.

Meanwhile, cut the bacon in half. Wrap a strip around each chicken breast and secure it underneath with a toothpick. Poke a sprig of fresh rosemary underneath the bacon. Heat a non-stick frying pan over medium heat. Spray with the oil. Cook the chicken for 2–3 minutes on each side, or until golden on both sides. Cover and cook for 10–15 minutes, or until the chicken is cooked through. Remove the toothpicks. Serve the chicken on the vegetables, surrounded with the sauce.

HINT: Serve with wholegrain bread or pasta for a filling, low-GI meal.

nutrition per serving Energy 359 Cal (1510 kJ); Fat 12.7 g; Saturated fat 3.5 g; Protein 50.6 g; Carbohydrate 8.6 g; Fiber 5.4 g; Cholesterol 132 mg

lamb casserole with beans

Casseroles are a great way to include a variety of legumes and vegetables in your diet, and are wonderful to warm you through on a cold winter's night.

1½ cups (10½ oz/300 g) dried borlotti or red kidney beans

2 lb 4 oz (1 kg) lean boned leg lamb

2 tsp olive oil

1¾ oz (50 g) low-fat bacon (we used 97% fat-free), chopped

1 large onion, chopped

2 garlic cloves, crushed

1 large carrot, chopped

2 cups (17 fl oz/500 ml) dry red wine

1 tbs tomato paste

1½ cups (13 fl oz/375 ml) beef stock

2 large sprigs rosemary

2 sprigs thyme

Prep time: 25 minutes + overnight soaking

Cooking time: 2¼ hours

Serves 6

Put the beans in a large bowl, cover with water and leave to soak overnight. Drain well.

Preheat the oven to 315°F (160°C/Gas 2–3). Trim any fat from the lamb and cut into bite-size cubes.

Heat the oil in a large flameproof casserole and brown the lamb in two batches over high heat for 2 minutes. Remove all the lamb from the dish and set aside. Add the bacon and onion to the casserole. Cook over medium heat for 3 minutes, or until the onion is soft. Add the garlic and carrot and cook for 1 minute, or until fragrant.

Return the lamb and any juices to the pan, increase the heat to high and add the wine. Bring to a boil and cook for 2 minutes. Add the beans, tomato paste, stock, rosemary and thyme, bring to a boil, then cover and cook in the oven for 2 hours, or until the meat is tender. Stir occasionally during cooking and skim off any fat from the surface. Season with salt and freshly ground black pepper and remove the herb sprigs before serving.

HINT: Serve with some pasta or grainy bread for a complete meal.

nutrition per serving Energy 460 Cal (1933 kJ); Fat 13.1 g; Saturated fat 5.3 g; Protein 51 g; Carbohydrate 23 g; Fiber 10.7 g; Cholesterol 113 mg

bombay curry with rice

Steak becomes an exotic dish simply by adding a mix of spices and coconut milk. Enticing aromas fill the kitchen while it is cooking.

2 tsp canola oil

2 onions, chopped

2 garlic cloves, crushed

2 green chilies, chopped

1 tbs grated fresh ginger

1½ tsp ground turmeric

1 tsp ground cumin

1 tbs ground coriander

½–1 tsp chili powder

2 lb 4 oz (1 kg) lean diced chuck steak

14 oz (400 g) can chopped tomatoes

1 cup (9 fl oz/250 ml) light coconut milk

2 cups (14 oz/400 g) basmati rice, rinsed and drained

small handful cilantro (coriander) leaves

Prep time: 20 minutes

Cooking time: 1 hour 50 minutes

Serves 6

Heat the oil in a large heavy-based saucepan and cook the onion for 2–3 minutes, or until just soft. Add the garlic, chili, ginger, turmeric, cumin, coriander and chili powder. Stir for 1–2 minutes, or until heated, then add the beef and cook, stirring, over high heat until well coated with the spice mixture.

Add the tomatoes and season with salt. Simmer, covered, for 1–1½ hours, or until the beef is tender. Stir in the coconut milk and simmer, uncovered, for a further 5–10 minutes, or until slightly thickened.

Meanwhile, put the rice and 4 cups (35 fl oz/1 liter) water in a saucepan and bring to a boil over medium heat. Reduce the heat to low, cover with a lid and cook for 20 minutes, or until the rice is tender. Remove from the heat and leave to stand, covered, for 5 minutes. Stir in the cilantro. Serve the rice with the curry.

HINTS: This curry is best made 1–2 days in advance to give the flavors time to develop. Store, covered, in the refrigerator.

If you have diabetes, you can reduce the GI of this dish even further by reducing the quantity of rice and adding some cooked brown lentils or barley.

nutrition per serving Energy 503 Cal (2111 kJ); Fat 11.1 g; Saturated fat 5 g; Protein 41.3 g; Carbohydrate 59.4 g; Fiber 3.5 g; Cholesterol 95 mg

pork, bok choy and black bean stir-fry

This meal is a good source of folate, beta-carotene, iron and zinc.

2 cups (14 oz/400 g) basmati rice, rinsed and drained

14 oz (400 g) lean pork leg steaks

2 tsp sesame oil

2 onions, thinly sliced

2 garlic cloves, finely chopped

2–3 tsp chopped fresh ginger

1 red pepper (capsicum), cut into strips

1 tbs canned salted black beans, rinsed, roughly chopped

1 lb 2 oz (500 g) baby bok choy, shredded

½ cup (3¼ oz/90 g) canned water chestnuts, rinsed, drained and thinly sliced

2 tbs oyster sauce

1 tbs soy sauce

2 tsp fish sauce

Prep time: 20 minutes
Cooking time: 35 minutes
Serves 4

Put the rice and 4 cups (35 fl oz/1 liter) water in a saucepan and bring to a boil over medium heat. Reduce the heat to low, cover with a lid and cook for 20 minutes, or until the rice is tender. Remove from the heat and leave to stand, covered, for 5 minutes.

Meanwhile, slice the pork steaks into strips across the grain. Heat a wok over medium–high heat until hot, add half the sesame oil and swirl to coat. Cook the onion, garlic and ginger over high heat for 3–4 minutes, being careful that the garlic doesn't burn. Add the pepper and cook for 2–3 minutes. Remove from the wok.

Heat the remaining sesame oil in the wok, add the pork in batches and stir-fry briefly until browned. Reheat the wok between batches.

Return all the pork to the pan with the onion mixture, black beans, bok choy, water chestnuts and oyster, soy and fish sauces. Toss quickly, reduce the heat, cover and steam for 3–4 minutes, or until the bok choy has just wilted. Serve with the rice.

nutrition per serving Energy 562 Cal (2361 kJ); Fat 7.2 g; Saturated fat 1.8 g; Protein 32.4 g; Carbohydrate 90.8 g; Fiber 4.5 g; Cholesterol 57 mg

hungarian-style
pork and lentil stew

This hearty European stew is satisfying and nutritious and tastes even better the next day as leftovers. You can serve it with pasta instead of rice, if preferred.

2 tsp olive oil

2 onions, chopped

1 lb 2 oz (500 g) lean diced pork

2 tsp sweet Hungarian paprika

1 tsp hot paprika

½ tsp dried thyme

2 tbs tomato paste

1 tsp soft brown sugar

¼ cup (2¼ oz/60 g) red lentils

1½ cups (13 fl oz/375 ml) beef stock

1 tomato

2 cups (14 oz/400 g) basmati rice, rinsed and drained

2 tbs low-fat plain yogurt

Prep time: 20 minutes

Cooking time: 1 hour 5 minutes

Serves 4

Heat the olive oil in a large, deep saucepan over high heat. Add the onion, pork and paprika and stir for 3–4 minutes, or until browned.

Add the thyme, tomato paste, sugar, lentils and stock and season with salt and freshly ground black pepper. Bring to a boil, reduce the heat to very low and cook, covered, for 20 minutes, stirring occasionally to prevent sticking. Uncover and cook for 15–20 minutes, or until thickened.

Remove from the heat and set aside for 10 minutes. To prepare the tomato, cut in half and then scoop out the seeds. Slice the flesh into thin strips.

Meanwhile, put the rice and 4 cups (35 fl oz/1 liter) water in a saucepan and bring to a boil over medium heat. Reduce the heat to low, cover with a lid and cook for 20 minutes, or until the rice is tender. Remove from the heat and leave to stand, covered, for 5 minutes.

Just before serving, stir the yogurt into the stew. Sprinkle with tomato. Serve with the rice and a salad.

nutrition per serving Energy 592 Cal (2485 kJ); Fat 6.5 g; Saturated fat 1.6 g; Protein 41.1 g; Carbohydrate 91.8 g; Fiber 5.1 g; Cholesterol 119 mg

pork with yardlong beans and noodles

Using fresh rice noodles instead of rice saves a lot of time and is also a simple way to lower the meal's GI.

14 oz (400 g) fresh thin rice noodles

14 oz (400 g) lean pork tenderloin (fillet)

2 tsp canola oil

2 onions, thinly sliced

5½ oz (150 g) yardlong (snake) beans, sliced on the diagonal

3 garlic cloves, finely chopped

1 tbs finely chopped fresh ginger

1 red pepper (capsicum), thinly sliced

6 scallions (spring onions), sliced on the diagonal

2 tbs sweet chili sauce

Prep time: 20 minutes
Cooking time: 20 minutes
Serves 4

Put the rice noodles in a large heatproof bowl, cover with boiling water and soak for 8 minutes, or until tender. Separate gently and drain.

Trim the pork and thickly slice. Heat a wok until very hot, add half the oil and swirl it around to coat the side. Add the pork and stir-fry in two batches over high heat for 3–4 minutes, or until it is just cooked, adding a little more oil if necessary for the second batch. Remove from the wok. Reheat the wok between batches.

Heat the remaining oil in the wok over medium heat and add the onion. Cook for 3–4 minutes, or until the onion has softened slightly. Add the yardlong beans and cook for 2–3 minutes. Add the garlic, ginger, pepper and scallion, and toss well. Add 2 tablespoons water and decrease the heat to medium. Cover and cook for 2–3 minutes, stirring frequently.

Return the pork to the wok, add the noodles, sweet chili sauce and 2 tablespoons extra water and toss well for 1–2 minutes. Remove from the heat and season with salt and freshly ground black pepper. Serve immediately with the noodles.

HINT: If you can't find yardlong beans you can use ordinary green beans in this recipe.

nutrition per serving Energy 370 Cal (1553 kJ); Fat 5.8 g; Saturated fat 1 g; Protein 28.5 g; Carbohydrate 50.3 g; Fiber 4 g; Cholesterol 95 mg

rogan josh

This famous Indian curry has a rich aroma and flavor and provides good amounts of protein, B vitamins and minerals.

2 lb 4 oz (1 kg) lean boned leg lamb

2 tsp canola oil

2 onions, chopped

½ cup (4½ oz/125 g) low-fat plain yogurt

1 tsp chili powder

1 tbs ground coriander

2 tsp ground cumin

1 tsp ground cardamom

1 tsp ground turmeric

½ tsp ground cloves

3 garlic cloves, crushed

1 tbs grated fresh ginger

14 oz (400 g) can chopped tomatoes

1 tsp salt

¼ cup (1 oz/30 g) slivered almonds

2 cups (14 oz/400 g) basmati rice, rinsed and drained

1 tsp garam masala

chopped cilantro (coriander) leaves, to serve

Prep time: 25 minutes

Cooking time: 2 hours

Serves 6

Trim the lamb of any fat or sinew and cut into small cubes. Heat the oil in a large heavy-based saucepan, add the onion and cook, stirring, for 5 minutes, or until soft. Stir in the yogurt, chili powder, coriander, cumin, cardamom, turmeric, cloves, garlic and ginger. Add the tomato and salt and simmer for 5 minutes.

Add the lamb and stir until coated. Cover and cook over low heat, stirring occasionally, for 1–1½ hours, or until the lamb is tender. Uncover and simmer until the liquid thickens.

Meanwhile, toast the almonds in a dry frying pan over medium heat for 3–4 minutes, shaking the pan gently, until the nuts are golden brown. Remove from the pan at once to prevent them burning.

Meanwhile, put the rice and 4 cups (35 fl oz/1 liter) water in a saucepan and bring to a boil over medium heat. Reduce the heat to low, cover with a lid and cook for 20 minutes, or until the rice is tender. Remove from the heat and leave to stand, covered, for 5 minutes.

Add the garam masala to the curry and mix through well. Sprinkle the slivered almonds and cilantro leaves over the top and serve with the rice.

HINT: If you have diabetes, you can reduce this meal's GI further by reducing the quantity of rice and adding some canned chickpeas.

nutrition per serving Energy 555 Cal (2330 kJ); Fat 15.2 g; Saturated fat 5.3 g; Protein 44.6 g; Carbohydrate 59.5 g; Fiber 3.4 g; Cholesterol 114 mg

chicken provençale

No wonder this dish is a French classic—the flavors are superb and it is warming and nourishing. It is a good source of protein and B vitamins.

2 tsp olive oil

3 lb 5 oz (1.5 kg) skinless chicken pieces

1 onion, chopped

1 red pepper (capsicum), chopped

2 garlic cloves, chopped

4 tbs white wine

4 tbs chicken stock

14 oz (400 g) can chopped tomatoes

2 tbs tomato paste

½ cup (3¼ oz/90 g) black olives in brine, drained

13 oz (375 g) fettuccine

small handful basil leaves, to garnish

Prep time: 15 minutes

Cooking time: 1 hour 35 minutes

Serves 6

Heat the oil in a large heavy-based saucepan over high heat, add the chicken, in batches, and cook for 3–4 minutes, or until browned. Return all the chicken to the pan and add the onion, pepper and garlic. Cook for 2–3 minutes, or until the onion is soft.

Add the wine, stock, tomatoes, tomato paste and olives and bring to a boil. Reduce the heat, cover and simmer for 30 minutes. Remove the lid, turn the chicken pieces over and cook for another 30 minutes, or until the chicken is tender and the sauce thickened.

Meanwhile, cook the pasta in a large saucepan of boiling water for 10 minutes, or until *al dente*. Drain well. Sprinkle the chicken with basil and serve with the pasta.

nutrition per serving Energy 464 Cal (1947 kJ); Fat 13.1 g; Saturated fat 3.7 g; Protein 33.3 g; Carbohydrate 50.7 g; Fiber 4 g; Cholesterol 115 mg

italian fish rolls with sweet potato

This meal is a delicious way to eat fish and is a good source of protein, beta-carotene and B vitamins.

1 large ripe tomato

1 tbs capers, drained and chopped

¼ cup (1½ oz/40 g) stuffed green olives in brine, drained and chopped

3 tbs finely chopped lemon thyme

¼ cup (1 oz/30 g) finely grated romano cheese

2 tsp finely grated lemon zest

¼ tsp freshly ground black pepper

8 thin white skinless fish fillets (about 1 lb 14 oz/850 g) *(see Hint)*

1 cup (9 fl oz/250 ml) white wine

2 tbs lemon juice

3 tbs lemon thyme

2 bay leaves

1 lb 12 oz (800 g) sweet potato, peeled and cut into 2 in (5 cm) pieces

Prep time: 30 minutes

Cooking time: 30 minutes

Serves 4–6

Preheat the oven to 315°F (160°C/Gas 2–3). To peel the tomatoes, score a cross in the base of each one. Cover with boiling water for 30 seconds, then plunge into cold water. Drain and peel away the skin from the cross. Cut in half and scoop out the seeds. Roughly chop the flesh and mix with the capers, olives, lemon thyme, cheese, lemon zest and pepper in a small bowl.

Place the fillets skinned-side-up on a flat surface. Spread the tomato mixture evenly onto each fillet, then roll up tightly and secure with a toothpick or skewer. Place in a single layer in a shallow casserole.

Pour the combined wine, juice, lemon thyme and bay leaves over the fish, cover with foil and bake for 20 minutes, or until the fish is cooked and flakes easily when tested with a fork.

Meanwhile, cook the sweet potato in a large saucepan of boiling salted water for 10 minutes or until cooked. Drain and roughly mash. Season well with salt and pepper. Serve with the fish rolls.

HINT: Use porgy, bream, perch or snapper or ask your fish seller for a suggestion.

nutrition per serving (6) Energy 287 Cal (1206 kJ); Fat 4.5 g; Saturated fat 1.8 g; Protein 33.7 g; Carbohydrate 20.7 g; Fiber 4.2 g; Cholesterol 91 mg

tuna with lime and chili sauce and green vegetables

This delicious meal is quick and easy to make and provides useful amounts of nutrients that many people don't eat enough of—omega-3 fatty acids, iron, zinc and other minerals.

SAUCE

2 large handfuls mint, chopped

2 large handfuls cilantro (coriander) leaves, chopped

1 tsp grated lime zest

1 tbs lime juice

1 tsp grated fresh ginger

1 jalapeno chili, seeded and finely chopped

1 cup (9 oz/250 g) low-fat plain yogurt

canola oil spray

4 tuna steaks

1 bunch (6 oz/175 g) asparagus, trimmed and cut into 2 in (5 cm) pieces

4½ oz (125 g) snow peas (mangetout), trimmed

4½ oz (125 g) green beans, trimmed

4 wholegrain bread rolls, to serve

Prep time: 20 minutes

Cooking time: 10 minutes

Serves 4

To make the sauce, mix together the mint, cilantro, lime zest, lime juice, ginger and chili. Fold in the yogurt and season with salt and freshly ground black pepper.

Heat a charbroil pan over high heat and lightly spray with the oil. Cook the tuna steaks for 2 minutes on each side, or until cooked, but still pink in the center.

Meanwhile, steam the vegetables for 2–3 minutes, or until just tender.

Top the tuna with the sauce. Serve with the vegetables and bread.

HINT: Jalapeno chilies are smooth and thick-fleshed and are available both red and green. They are quite fiery, so you can use a less powerful variety of chili if you prefer.

nutrition per serving Energy 452 Cal (1896 kJ); Fat 12.2 g; Saturated fat 4 g; Protein 51.9 g; Carbohydrate 32.5 g; Fiber 6 g; Cholesterol 61 mg

chili con pollo

This easy recipe is the chicken lover's version of chili con carne.

2 tsp olive oil

1 onion, finely chopped

1 lb 2 oz (500 g) lean ground (minced) chicken

1–2 tsp mild chili powder

14 oz (400 g) can chopped tomatoes

2 tbs tomato paste

14 oz (400 g) can red kidney beans, drained and rinsed

2 cups (14 oz/400 g) basmati rice, rinsed and drained

4 tbs chopped parsley

1 cup (9 oz/250 g) low-fat plain yogurt

Prep time: 10 minutes

Cooking time: 1 hour

Serves 4

Heat the oil in a large saucepan. Add the onion and cook over medium heat for 3 minutes, or until soft. Increase the heat and add the chicken. Cook until browned, breaking up any lumps with a wooden spoon.

Add the chili powder and cook for 1 minute. Add the tomato, tomato paste and ½ cup (4 fl oz/125 ml) water and stir well. Bring to a boil, then reduce the heat and simmer for 30 minutes. Stir in the kidney beans and heat through. Season to taste with salt and freshly ground black pepper.

Meanwhile, put the rice and 4 cups (35 fl oz/1 liter) water in a saucepan and bring to a boil over medium heat. Reduce the heat to low, cover with a lid and cook for 20 minutes, or until the rice is tender. Remove from the heat and leave to stand, covered, for 5 minutes.

Sprinkle the chili con pollo with the parsley and serve with the yogurt and rice.

nutrition per serving Energy 683 Cal (2871 kJ); Fat 13.8 g; Saturated fat 3.6 g; Protein 40.3 g; Carbohydrate 98 g; Fiber 7.5 g; Cholesterol 116 mg

spaghetti marinara

This dish is an easy way to include fish and seafood in your diet. If you're short of time, you can use 1 lb 2 oz (500 g) fresh or frozen ready-made marinara mix as a substitute for the mussels, squid, fish and shrimp.

4½ oz (125 g) small squid hoods

4½ oz (125 g) skinless firm white fish fillets

7 oz (200 g) raw shrimp (prawns)

12 mussels

2 tsp olive oil

1 onion, chopped

2 garlic cloves, crushed

½ cup (4 fl oz/125 ml) red wine

2 tbs tomato paste

14 oz (400 g) can chopped tomatoes

1 cup (9 fl oz/250 ml) bottled tomato pasta sauce

1 tbs each of chopped basil and oregano

¾ oz (20 g) canola oil margarine

1 lb 2 oz (500 g) spaghetti

Prep time: 50 minutes
Cooking time: 30 minutes
Serves 4

To prepare the seafood, slice the squid hoods into rings. Cut the fish into bite-size cubes, checking for bones. Peel the shrimp, leaving the tails intact. Gently pull out the dark vein from each shrimp back, starting at the head end. Scrub the mussels with a stiff brush and pull out the hairy beards. Discard any that are broken or open ones that don't close when tapped on the bench.

Heat the olive oil in a large saucepan. Add the onion and garlic and cook over low heat for 2–3 minutes. Increase the heat to medium and add the wine, tomato paste, tomato and pasta sauce. Simmer, stirring occasionally, for 5–10 minutes, or until the sauce reduces and thickens slightly. Stir in the herbs and season to taste. Keep warm.

While the sauce is simmering, heat ½ cup (4 fl oz/125 ml) water in a saucepan. Add the mussels, cover and steam for 3–5 minutes, or until the mussels have changed color and opened. Remove from the pan, discarding any mussels that haven't opened, and stir the liquid into the tomato sauce.

Heat the margarine in a frying pan and sauté the squid, fish and shrimp in batches, for 1–2 minutes, or until cooked. Add the seafood to the warm tomato sauce and stir gently.

Meanwhile, cook the pasta in a large saucepan of boiling water for 10 minutes, or until *al dente*. Drain well. Toss the seafood sauce with the pasta and serve immediately with a mixed leaf salad.

nutrition per serving Energy 664 Cal (2790 kJ); Fat 10 g; Saturated fat 3.9 g; Protein 39.5 g; Carbohydrate 97.5 g; Fiber 7.9 g; Cholesterol 154 mg

steamed lemon grass and ginger chicken with asian greens

This satisfying meal of tender aromatic steamed chicken is rich in protein, folate, antioxidants and potassium.

7 oz (200 g) fresh thin rice noodles

4 boneless, skinless chicken breasts, trimmed

2 stems lemon grass

2 in (5 cm) piece fresh ginger, julienned

1 lime, thinly sliced

2 cups (17 fl oz/500 ml) chicken stock

1 bunch (12 oz/350 g) choy sum, cut into 4 in (10 cm) lengths

1 lb 12 oz (800 g) Chinese broccoli (gai larn), cut into 4 in (10 cm) lengths

3 tbs kecap manis

3 tbs soy sauce

1 tsp sesame oil

toasted sesame seeds, to garnish

Prep time: 25 minutes
Cooking time: 40 minutes
Serves 4

Put the rice noodles in a large heatproof bowl, cover with boiling water and soak for 5 minutes, or until softened. Separate gently and drain. Cut each chicken breast horizontally through the middle so that you are left with eight thin flat chicken pieces.

Cut the lemon grass into lengths that are about 2 in (5 cm) longer than the chicken breasts, then cut in half lengthwise. Discard tough outer leaves. Place one piece of lemon grass onto one breast, top with some ginger and lime slices, then top with the other breast.

Pour the stock into a wok and bring to a simmer. Put two of the chicken breasts in a paper-lined bamboo steamer. Place the steamer over the wok and steam over the simmering stock for 12–15 minutes, or until the chicken is tender. Remove the chicken from the steamer, cover and keep warm. Repeat with the other breasts.

Steam the greens in the same way for 3 minutes, or until tender. Bring the stock in the wok to a boil. Place the kecap manis, soy sauce and sesame oil in a bowl and whisk together well.

Divide the noodles among four plates and ladle the boiling stock over them. Top with a pile of Asian greens, then add the chicken and drizzle each serve with the sauce. Sprinkle with sesame seeds and serve.

HINT: Kecap manis is an Indonesian sweet sauce similar to a soy sauce.

nutrition per serving Energy 438 Cal (1839 kJ); Fat 13.7 g; Saturated fat 3.8 g; Protein 51.2 g; Carbohydrate 27.1 g; Fiber 4.6 g; Cholesterol 132 mg

cioppino

This delicious stew, made with tomatoes, fish and seafood is rich in color and flavor and is a good source of protein, B vitamins and minerals. For some extra heat, you can add some chili flakes.

2 dried shiitake mushrooms

2 lb 4 oz (1 kg) skinless white fish fillets

13 oz (375 g) raw large shrimp (prawns)

1 raw lobster tail (about 14 oz/400 g)

12–15 black mussels

1 tbs olive oil

1 large onion, finely chopped

1 green pepper (capsicum), finely chopped

2–3 garlic cloves, crushed

14 oz (400 g) can chopped tomatoes

1 cup (9 fl oz/250 ml) white wine

1 cup (9 fl oz/250 ml) unsweetened tomato juice

1 cup (9 fl oz/250 ml) fish stock

1 bay leaf

2 sprigs parsley

2 tsp chopped basil

1 tbs chopped parsley, extra

Prep time: 30 minutes + 20 minutes soaking

Cooking time: 1 hour

Serves 4

Put the mushrooms in a small bowl, cover with boiling water and leave to soak for 20 minutes. Drain, squeeze dry and chop finely.

Cut the fish into bite-size pieces, checking for bones. Peel the shrimp, leaving the tails intact. Gently pull out the dark vein from each shrimp back, starting at the head end. Starting at the end where the head was, cut down the sides of the lobster shell on the underside of the lobster with kitchen scissors. Pull back the flap, remove the meat from the shell and cut into small pieces. Scrub the mussels with a stiff brush and pull out the hairy beards. Discard any broken mussels, or open ones that don't close when tapped on the bench. Rinse well.

Heat the oil in a heavy-based pan, add the onion, pepper and garlic and stir over medium heat for about 5 minutes, or until the onion is soft. Add the mushrooms, tomato, wine, tomato juice, stock, bay leaf, parsley sprigs and basil. Bring to a boil, reduce the heat, then cover and simmer for 30 minutes.

Layer the fish and shrimp in a large deep-sided frying pan. Add the sauce, then cover and leave on low heat for 10 minutes, or until the shrimp are pink and the fish is cooked. Add the lobster and mussels and simmer for another 4–5 minutes. Season with salt and freshly ground black pepper. Discard any unopened mussels. Sprinkle with parsley. Serve with pasta

HINT: Try snapper, monkfish, perch or cod.

nutrition per serving Energy 493 Cal (2071 kJ); Fat 10.4 g; Saturated fat 2.6 g; Protein 75.6 g; Carbohydrate 13.3 g; Fiber 2.9 g; Cholesterol 274 mg

lamb souvlaki

For color and variety, you can add some onion and green pepper pieces to these delicious marinated Greek lamb skewers.

2 tsp olive oil

2 tsp finely grated lemon zest

4 tbs lemon juice

2 tsp dried oregano

½ cup (4 fl oz/125 ml) dry white wine

3 garlic cloves, finely chopped

2 fresh bay leaves

2 lb 4 oz (1 kg) boned leg lamb

1 cup (9 oz/250 g) low-fat plain yogurt

2 garlic cloves, crushed, extra

olive oil spray

4 stoneground whole wheat (wholemeal) pita breads, to serve

Prep time: 20 minutes + overnight marinating
Cooking time: 10 minutes
Serves 4

To make the marinade, combine the olive oil, lemon zest and juice, oregano, wine, garlic, bay leaves and salt and freshly ground black pepper in a large non-metallic bowl. Trim the lamb and cut into bite-size cubes. Add to the marinade and toss to coat well. Cover and refrigerate overnight.

Put the yogurt and extra garlic in a bowl, mix together well and leave for 30 minutes. If using wooden skewers, soak for 30 minutes beforehand to prevent scorching.

Drain the lamb and pat dry. Thread onto 8 metal or wooden skewers. Heat the barbecue hotplate, and spray with the oil, cook and turn frequently for 7–8 minutes, or until evenly brown on the outside and still a little rare in the middle.

Meanwhile, wrap the breads in foil and put in a warm place on the barbecue for 10 minutes to heat through.

Drizzle the skewers with the garlic yogurt and serve on the warm pita bread with a green salad.

nutrition per serving Energy 632 Cal (2654 kJ); Fat 19.9 g; Saturated fat 8 g; Protein 65.2 g; Carbohydrate 41.6 g; Fiber 6 g; Cholesterol 172 mg

chicken with tomatoes, olives and capers

This Mediterranean dish is suitable at any time of the year and is particularly delicious topped with fresh basil.

olive oil spray

1 red onion, cut into thin wedges

1 celery stalk, sliced

5½ oz (150 g) mushrooms, sliced

3–4 garlic cloves, thinly sliced

all-purpose (plain) flour, for dusting

4 boneless, skinless chicken breasts, trimmed

2 tsp olive oil

½ cup (4 fl oz/125 ml) white wine

10½ fl oz (300 ml) chicken stock

14 oz (400 g) can chopped tomatoes

1 tbs tomato paste

⅓ cup (2¼ oz/60 g) black olives in brine, drained

1 tbs capers

13 oz (375 g) fettuccine

Prep time: 20 minutes
Cooking time: 1 hour 10 minutes
Serves 4

Heat a large non-stick frying pan and spray with oil. Add the onion, celery, mushrooms and garlic and cook, stirring, for 5 minutes, or until the onion is soft. Add 1 tablespoon of water to prevent sticking if necessary. Remove from the pan.

Season the flour with salt and freshly ground black pepper. Lightly toss the chicken in the flour, shaking off the excess. Heat the oil in the frying pan and cook the chicken, turning once, for 5 minutes, or until well browned. Add the wine and stock and cook for a further 2 minutes.

Return the vegetables to the pan and add the tomato and tomato paste. Simmer, partially covered, for 30–40 minutes, or until thickened. Add the olives and capers and season with salt and freshly ground black pepper.

Meanwhile, cook the fettuccine in a large saucepan of boiling water for 10 minutes, or until *al dente*. Drain and serve with the chicken. Serve the meal with a mixed leaf salad.

nutrition per serving Energy 715 Cal (3001 kJ); Fat 15.6 g; Saturated fat 4.2 g; Protein 59 g; Carbohydrate 78.3 g; Fiber 6.1 g; Cholesterol 149 mg